General Certificate of Secondar

GCSE Maths

is Easy Practice Papers Full Sets 1 & 2 – *Higher Tier*

How to pass GCSE Mathematics the easy way with full mock practice exams, marking sheets, and insider advice from maths teachers.

CONTENTS

how2become

As part of this product, you have also received FREE access to online tests that will help you to

pass GCSE MATHS Practice Papers
(Higher Tier).

To gain access, simply go to:

www.MyEducationalTests.co.uk

Get more products
for passing any test at:

www.How2Become.com

Orders: Please contact How2become Ltd, Suite 14, 50 Churchill Square Business Centre, Kings Hill, Kent ME19 4YU.

You can order through Amazon.co.uk under ISBN 9781910602836, via the website www.How2Become.com or through Gardners.com.

ISBN: 9781910602836

First published in 2016 by How2Become Ltd.

Copyright © 2016 How2Become.

Updated in 2017

Typeset for How2Become Ltd by Anton Pshinka.

Disclaimer

Every effort has been made to ensure that the information contained within this guide is accurate at the time of publication. How2Become is not responsible for anyone failing any part of any selection process as a result of the information contained within this guide. How2Become Ltd and their authors cannot accept any responsibility for any errors or omissions within this guide, however caused. No responsibility for loss or damage occasioned by any person acting, or refraining from action, as a result of the material in this publication can be accepted by How2Become Ltd.

The information within this guide does not represent the views of any third party service or organisation.

Using your papers

Read the instructions **carefully** before working through the practice papers.

In this book, there are **two** sets of practice papers:

Set A and **Set B**

Each **SET** includes:

➤ **A GCSE Mathematics Formula Sheet**

➤ **Paper 1 – Non-Calculator**   Marks out of 100
*Calculator **NOT** permitted*
1 hour 45 minutes

➤ **Paper 2 – Calculator**   Marks out of 100
*Calculator **IS** permitted*
1 hour 45 minutes

➤ **Answer Booklet**

PLEASE NOTE!

The number of marks and the time limit provided in these practice papers are for you to use as a **GUIDELINE ONLY**. They do not reflect the actual duration or the mark scheme of your Maths (Higher Tier) GCSE examination.

COMPLETING YOUR PRACTICE PAPERS

In order to complete these practice papers, you will need the following:

➤ GCSE Mathematics Formula Sheet (provided at the beginning of your practice papers)

➤ Pen

➤ Pencil

➤ Eraser

➤ A ruler

➤ A protractor

➤ A pair of compasses

➤ Tracing paper

➤ A calculator (for paper 2 ONLY).

PREPARING FOR YOUR MATHS GCSE

GCSE Maths Is Easy Practice Papers (Higher Tier) has been specifically designed to complement your classroom and home-based learning, prior to your GCSE Maths examination.

These practice papers should be used to help you revise the content and skills, which have already been taught to you in the classroom. Moreover, these papers will allow you to see which questions you are getting right, and which ones you are getting wrong. This will help you to tailor your revision to your weakest areas, to ensure you are fully prepared for your GCSE examination.

REMEMBER!

Practice *really* does make perfect.

The more you practice, the more marks you will score!

HOW TO WORK THROUGH YOUR PAPERS

In order to make the most out of your practice papers, consider the following:

STEP 1

Undergo one practice exam (one exam consists of both the Calculator and Non-Calculator paper).

STEP 2

Go through your answers and mark your work using the mark scheme provided.

STEP 3

Have a look at what questions you are getting wrong. These are the questions that you need to work on!

STEP 4

Practice these types of question again and then undertake another practice test. If you are still getting those questions wrong, keep practising. Keep revising that subject area until you get them all correct!

STEP 5

Work on **ALL** of your weak areas until you feel confident enough to tackle your GCSE Maths exam with ease.

STEP 6

Be sure to keep testing yourself. Every time you get a question wrong, consider *'why'* you got it wrong. Did you understand the question? Did you miscalculate? Did you know how to work the question out? Work out why you got the question wrong, and learn from your mistakes. Practice these questions thoroughly until you are confident enough to tackle and conquer every single one!

Calculating your grade

THE IMPORTANCE OF CALCULATING YOUR GRADE

Calculating your grade is an extremely important step in regards to GCSE preparation. By monitoring your performance, you are able to keep track of your progression and determine your strong areas, and more importantly, your weaker areas!

Calculating your grade in practice papers will give you some indication as to what grade or level you are currently working at. However, we CANNOT provide a guarantee that the grade you score in these practice papers will be the same as your actual exam. Your actual exam will use a very specific marking scheme and the grade boundaries may be slightly different, but our papers will give you some indication in regards to exam structure.

HOW TO WORK OUT YOUR GRADE

The optimal way to monitor your performance is to mark your practice papers as you go.

➢ Once you have completed a whole exam (Calculator and Non-Calculator paper), mark your answers using the mark scheme provided.

➢ All of the papers contained within this guide have a total score of 100. This allows you to easily calculate your percentage.

➢ Mark paper 1 and work out your percentage score. Mark paper 2 and work out your percentage score. Find your average percentage for the whole exam (paper 1 and paper 2).

➢ Using the table below, work out what grade represents your average percentage.

WORKING OUT YOUR AVERAGE %

To work out your average percentage, add up both percentages (for paper 1 and paper 2), and then divide by 2.

AVERAGE PERCENTAGE AND GRADE

Using your average percentage, work out what grade you achieved.

Average %	85+		69-84	46-68		32-45	15-31		Under 15
New grading system	9	8	7	6	5	4	3		U
Old grading system	A*		A	B		C	D	E	U

Please note: the above scoring system does not necessarily reflect the actual grading system of exam boards and should be used as guidance only. It is recommend to check with your exam board for their exact scoring system.

EXAMPLE

Here is an example of how to work out your average percentage. Say you scored the following in each paper:

➢ *74 marks out of 100 (paper 1: Non-Calculator)*

➢ *84 marks out of 100 (paper 2: Calculator)*

To work out your average:

➢ Because both papers are out of 100, these marks are already in percentages – 74% and 84%.

➢ To work out your average percentage, add up both percentages:

   74 + 84 = 158

> ➢ Now divide the total by 2:
>
> $158 \div 2 = 79$.
>
> ➢ Using the table above, find which bracket '79' comes under. This is equivalent to a grade 7 or 8.

RECORDING YOUR SCORES

By keeping a record of your marks/grades in the tables below, you will be able to keep track of your performance.

We recommend that you practice each practice paper **more than once**. That way you should be able to see your results improving.

The saying that *'practice makes perfect'* is spot-on when it comes to preparing for exams. Ultimately, the more you practice, the better your scores will be.

Practice Papers Set A

Write your scores and grades to practice papers A in the table below. We have provided you with additional space in case you attempt these papers more than once. This will allow you to monitor your performance and progression.

		Paper 1 %	Paper 2 %	Average %	Grade
Practice Papers A	1st attempt				
	2nd attempt				
	3rd attempt				

10

Practice Papers Set B

Write your scores and grades to practice papers B in the table below. We have provided you with additional space in case you attempt these papers more than once. This will allow you to monitor your performance and progression.

		Paper 1 %	Paper 2 %	Average %	Grade
Practice Papers B	1st attempt				
	2nd attempt				
	3rd attempt				

PLEASE NOTE

The grades you achieve in the practice papers are **NOT** a guarantee of achieving that grade in the real exam. They should merely be used as a guideline in regards to the level you are working at.

UNDERSTANDING THE GRADE BOUNDARIES

Please be aware that this book is for the Higher Tier GCSE Maths exam.

You should already know whether you are going to be sitting the Foundation Tier or Higher Tier paper.

Please be sure that you know which tier paper you will be sitting for your GCSE Maths examination.

Higher Tier

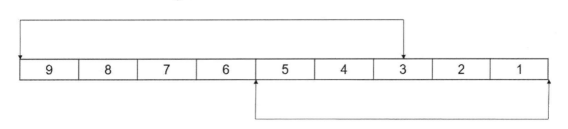

Foundation Tier

Guidance for GCSE

Exams are a stressful time for every student. In the lead-up to your exams, it is common for you to be feeling nervous. What you need is a unique survival guide. Use the tips below to aid you during your GCSE exam preparation.

STAGE 1 - REVISION

WHEN SHOULD I START REVISING FOR MY GCSES?

You can make your life so much easier by preparing for your GCSEs in advance. By preparing early, you will be able to overcome exam nerves and stress, therefore improving your overall performance when it comes to the actual exam.

If you spread your revision out over a prolonged period of time, you:

➢ Will be able to prepare and practice and ultimately improve your performance.

➢ Will reduce the amount of stress that you will be feeling in regards to your exams.

➢ Will be under less pressure and will be able to revise in a more efficient way.

➢ Will be able to enjoy free time. By not cramming in revision, you will still be able to relax and enjoy yourself.

HOW TO USE YOUR REVISION TIME WISELY

When it comes to exams, the majority of students will have to organise their time efficiently in order to make the most out of their learning.

Students will likely be facing numerous exams across a short period, and therefore they need to be able to break up their revision and set aside time for each subject.

Using a timetable can really help you to manage your time wisely.

➢ Work out how many exams you have to revise for.

➢ Take all of these subjects into consideration when creating your timetable, so that you spend a sufficient amount of time on each subject area.

➢ Be sure to make time for breaks and relaxation. You do not want to overload your brain!

➢ Make sure you factor in all your commitments such as lessons, social activities and free time.

On the next page, we have provided you with a timetable that you should fill in to help you organise your time. Only you will know what areas you need to work on, so make sure that your timetable reflects this.

REVISION TIMETABLE

Week Beginning: _____

	Monday	Tuesday	Wednesday	Thursday	Friday	Saturday	Sunday
9am							
10am							
11am							
12 noon							
1pm							
2pm							
3pm							
4pm							
5pm							
6pm							
7pm							
8pm							

*You will need to fill in this timetable for every week leading up to your exams. Once you sit an exam, you can take that out of your timetable, and spend more time on something else.

STAGE 2 - THE NIGHT BEFORE YOUR EXAM

NO MORE CRAMMING!

When the night before the exam comes around, you should **STOP** revising. If you continue revising the night before, you will do yourself no favours. You will feel more stressed, more pressured and more tired – none of which will better your performance.

THINGS TO CONSIDER

The night before the exam:

➢ Ensure that you have all of the equipment you need for your exam (pens, pencils, rubbers, protractors, rulers etc.).

➢ Double check your exam timetable so that you know what the start time is and where the exam is being held.

➢ Have a relaxing bath, and try not to think about the exam.

➢ Try to get an early night. This will allow you to wake up feeling refreshed and ready to go!

STAGE 3 – IN YOUR EXAM

Whilst your brain will be focused on trying to remember everything you have learned in the last few weeks, there are a few things you need to be aware of.

LISTEN!

An invigilator will start the exam by running through the exam procedures. Pay attention to what the invigilator is saying, as this may answer some of the questions or queries you have about the exam.

When invited to do so, you will need to fill in the front of your examination booklet. The front of your examination paper contains lots of information, which you will need to read carefully.

INSTRUCTIONS TO CANDIDATES:

➢ Before you begin filling in the front of your examination booklet, make sure that you have the correct test paper in front of you.

  o Make sure that the paper is for the correct subject (i.e. GCSE Mathematics).

  o Make sure that you are sitting the correct tier (i.e. foundation or higher).

  o Make sure you have all of the papers required for the exam (i.e. Non-Calculator, Calculator, Formula Sheet).

➢ Fill in ALL of your details on the front of your examination booklet. This will usually consist of the following:

  o Surname.

  o First Name/s.

  o Candidate Signature.

  o Candidate Number *(this will be provided to you on the day)*.

  o Centre Name and Number *(this will be provided to you on the day)*.

➢ Answer **ALL** of the questions in the spaces provided.

➢ When it comes to calculations, make sure you show **ALL** of your workings out.

➢ If you have any questions, raise your hand and wait for someone to assist.

ACTION CHECKLIST!

➢ Work through the paper at a steady pace.

➢ If you have any questions about the exam, be sure to raise your hand and wait for someone to assist you.

➢ Double check you have the correct exam paper in front of you.

➢ Make sure you have all of the correct equipment in order to complete the exam.

➢ Don't spend too long on one question.

➢ If you have time at the end, go back through the paper and check your work.

- Have a bottle of water nearby.
- Use a watch to monitor your time.
- Don't panic! You are ready! You are prepared!

STAGE 4 – AFTER YOUR EXAM

AFTER YOUR EXAM, *DO:*

- Reward yourself with some free time. Even if you have other exams coming up, you should spend some time doing something you enjoy. Just relax!
- Forget about the exam. It's over. There is no point dwelling about what you could have done, or what you didn't do.
- Be positive and proud. If you put that extra time and hard work into preparing for your exam, then you have done your best, and that's all you can do.

AFTER YOUR EXAM, *DON'T:*

- Do a post mortem of your exam. Do not pick your exam apart. Do not think about the *'what ifs'.* The exam is over. You cannot change anything now, so try not to worry.
- Discuss the exam with your friends. Discussing the exam and then thinking *'I didn't write that'* or *'I should have done that'*, will make you feel disheartened. Try to avoid any conversation about the contents of the exam.
- Worry yourself. Everyone comes out of exams fearing the worse. This is a common feeling amongst students, and chances are, you are worrying over nothing.
- Feel upset or disheartened if the exam didn't go according to plan. There are several opportunities for re-sits, and who knows, you may have done better than expected!

Prepare! Practice! Persevere!

GCSE Mathematics

SET A
Paper 1 Non-Calculator

Higher Tier
1 hour and 45 minutes

INSTRUCTIONS TO CANDIDATES

- Use **black** ink.
- **Fill in the boxes** at the top of this page.
- Answer **all** of the questions.
- **Clearly** show your workings out.

INFORMATION FOR CANDIDATES

- The **total mark** for this paper is **100**.
- The marks for each question are shown on the **right** side of each page.
- Questions labelled with an asterisk (*) will assess the **quality** of **written communication**.

ADVICE FOR CANDIDATES

- Keep a close eye on the **time**.
- **Do not** spend too long on one question.
- Try to answer **every** question and show your workings out when required.

Q	Attempt No.			Q	Attempt No.		
	1	2	3		1	2	3
1				12			
2				13			
3				14			
4				15			
5				16			
6				17			
7				18			
8				19			
9				20			
10				21			
11							
TOTAL							

For examiner's use

GCSE Mathematics

Higher Tier

Formula Sheet

Volume of cone $= \frac{1}{3}\pi r^2 h$

Curved surface area of cone $= \pi r l$

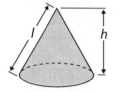

Volume of sphere $= \frac{4}{3}\pi r^3$

Surface area of sphere $= 4\pi r^2$

Volume of prism = area of cross section x length

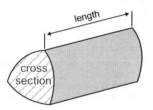

In any triangle *ABC*

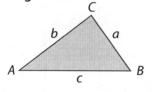

The Quadratic Equation

The solutions of $ax^2 + bx + c = 0$
where $a \neq 0$, are given by

$$x = \frac{-b \pm \sqrt{(b^2 - 4ac)}}{2a}$$

Sine Rule $\quad \dfrac{a}{\sin A} = \dfrac{b}{\sin B} = \dfrac{c}{\sin C}$

Cosine Rule $\quad a^2 = b^2 + c^2 - 2bc \cos A$

Area of triangle $= \frac{1}{2} ab \sin C$

Answer ALL questions.
Write your answers in the spaces provided.

1. Estimate the answer to the calculation below. You must show your working.

$$\frac{4805 \times 0.213}{5.236 + 4.721}$$

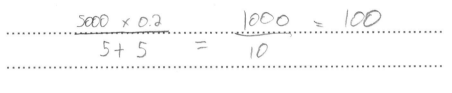

$$\frac{5000 \times 0.2}{5 + 5} = \frac{1000}{10} = 100$$

(3 marks)

2. **(a) (i)** Insert brackets to make this calculation correct.

$$4 \times (12 \div 3) = 16$$

(1 mark)

(ii) Insert brackets to make this calculation correct.

$$2 \times (30 - 14) = 32$$

(1 mark)

***(iii)** Andy says that $4 \times 3 - 2 \times 7 = -2$

Ryan says the answer to this calculation is 70.

Who is correct, and explain your reasons why.

(2 marks)

3. The diagram below shows the landscape of a field. The area of the landscape is 188 m².

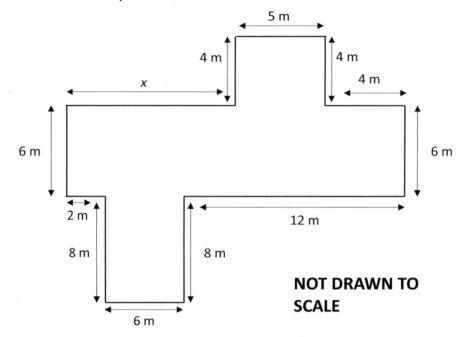

NOT DRAWN TO SCALE

Work out the value of x.

....

(4 marks)

4. (a) Write the following number in standard form:

524,000

....

(a)..

(1 mark)

(b) What is 0.000008 in standard form?

....

....

....

(b)..

(2 marks)

(c) Calculate the following

$(5.5 \times 10^7) - (3.14 \times 10^4)$

Give your answer in standard form.

....

....

....

(c)..

(2 marks)

5. Tessa, Holly and Julie have a bag of counters.

There are 8 orange, 10 yellow and 6 pink counters in the bag.

(a) What is the probability of picking a counter that is either orange or pink?

....

(a)..

(1 mark)

(b) Tessa says, "I don't want any orange counter".

What is the probability of Tessa picking a colour that she wants?

....

(b)..

(1 mark)

(c) What is the fraction of pink counters out of the total of counters in the bag? Give your answer in its simplest form.

....

(c)..

(1 mark)

(d) 6 more counters are added into the bag. These counters are 2 different colours to what's already in the bag. There are now 5 colours in the bag. What is the probability of picking a new colour counter from the bag?

....

(d)..

(1 mark)

6. The below table and histogram shows information about the number of times pupils arrived late to school. The study is out of 136 people.

Mark (n%)	Frequency
$0 < n \leq 2$	10
$2 < n \leq 3$	18
$3 < n \leq 5$	
$5 < n \leq 6$	30
$6 < n \leq 7$	
$7 < n \leq 10$	30

(a) Use the table above to complete the histogram.

(2 marks)

(b) Use the histogram to complete the table.

(2 marks)

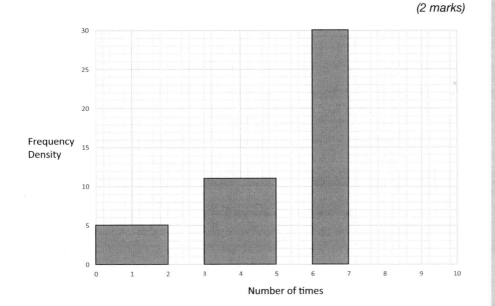

Number of times

7. David is the Operations Manager of a book publishing company.

He is conducting self-evaluations with each team member. There are 8 employees who David must spend time with.

These self-evaluations need to be completed in a 5 hour period, with a short break of 10 minutes between each person. Each person will be self-evaluated individually.

(a) Work out the maximum amount of time David can spend on each person's self-evaluation. Give your answer to the nearest minute.

....

....

....

....

(a)..

(3 marks)

(b) Michael is saving money to buy his first house. Currently, Michael has £3,800 in his bank account. His bank account pays 5% compound interest each year.

   (i) How much money will Michael have after 2 years?

....

....

(b) (i)..

(1 mark)

(ii) How many years will it take Michael to reach over £5,000? Only use the whole pounds in his account each year.

....

(b) (ii)..

(2 marks)

8. (a) Below is a semi-circle which has a diameter of 48 cm.

Work out the perimeter of the semi-circle.

Use the approximation that Pi = 3.1

NOT DRAWN TO SCALE

48 cm

....

....

....

....

....

....

....

....

(a)...

(3 marks)

(b) Below is a circle.

Find the circumference and the area. Use the estimation that Pi = 3.1

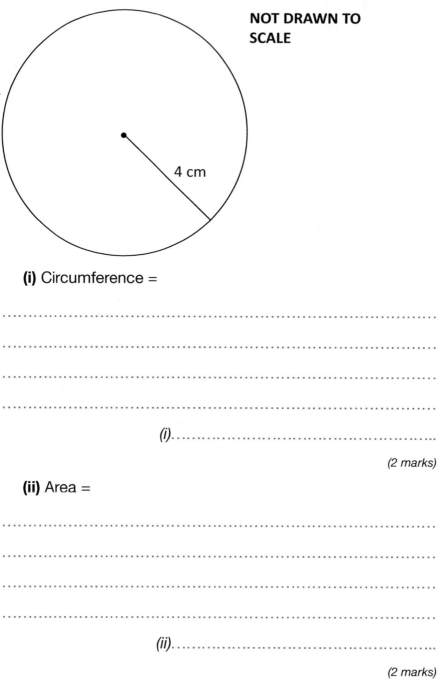

NOT DRAWN TO SCALE

4 cm

(i) Circumference =

....

....

....

....

(i)..

(2 marks)

(ii) Area =

....

....

....

....

(ii)..

(2 marks)

9. (a) AB and CD are parallel straight lines.

EF and GH are equal.

Work out the value of x.

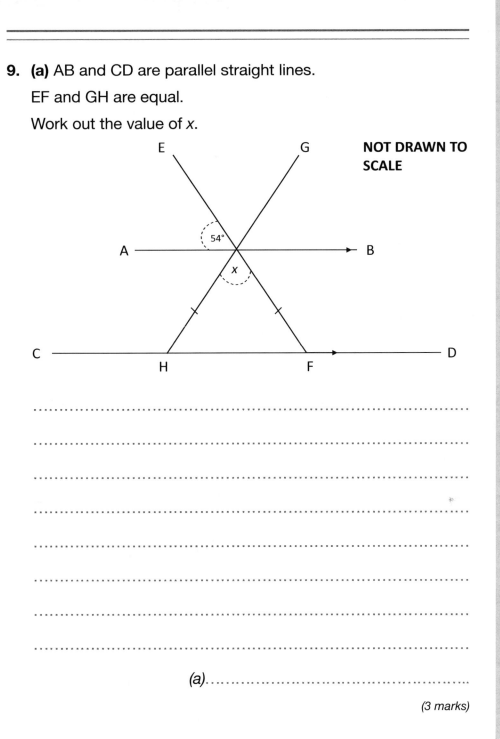

NOT DRAWN TO SCALE

....

....

....

....

....

....

....

....

(a)...

(3 marks)

(b) Lines AB and CD are parallel.

Lines GH and EF are the same length.

Work out the value of x.

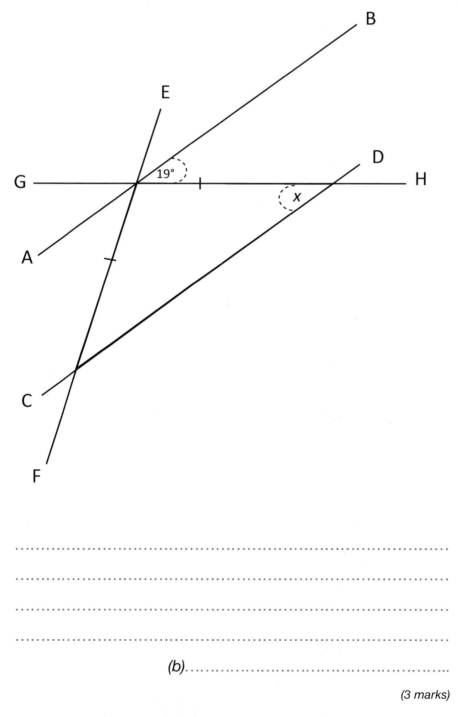

....

....

....

....

(b)..

10. (a) A scale of a map is 1 : 30,000. A distance is measured as 4 cm on the map.

How many centimetres, metres and kilometres is this equivalent based on the scale of the map?

(i) Centimetres =

....

....

(i)...

(1 mark)

(ii) Metres =

....

....

(ii)...

(1 mark)

(iii) Kilometres =

....

....

(iii)...

(1 mark)

11. Solve the simultaneous equations:

(a) (i) 4a + 2b = 22

6a − 2b = 28

....

....

a = ...

(1 mark)

....

....

b = ...

(1 mark)

(ii) 2a + 5b = 33

a + 3b = 19

....

....

a = ...

(1 mark)

....

....

b = ...

(1 mark)

(iii) $4a - 6b = 0$

$6a + 2b = 22$

....

....

$a = $ ....

(2 marks)

....

....

$b = $ ....

(2 marks)

12. On the grid below, plot the graph which represents the following:

$x + y = 4$ with values of x from -1 to 4

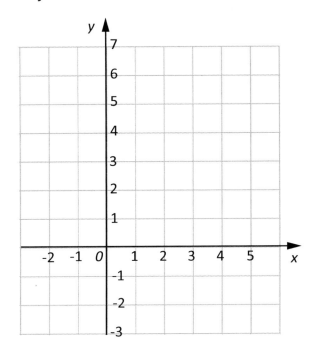

(4 marks)

13. (a) Find the Lowest Common Multiple of 8 and 12.

....

....

....

(2 marks)

(b) Find the Highest Common Factor of 72 and 48.

....

....

....

(2 marks)

(c) Express 54 as a product of its prime factors.

....

....

....

(2 marks)

14. The table below gives some indication of probability in regards to a pack of playing cards. Please note, for the purpose of this game, the Ace is high.

Outcome	Number of ways to achieve this outcome	Total number of possible outcomes	Probability
Choosing a 'numbered' card	36	52	$^{36}/_{52}$ or $^{9}/_{13}$
Choosing a 'face' card			
The card being between 5 and 9			

(a) Fill in the rest of the table.

(2 marks)

(b) Elizabeth plays a game with a pack of cards. She has a deck of cards, and turns one card over each time. The aim of the game is to determine whether the next card is going to be higher of lower. For the purpose of this game, the 'Ace' is high.

(i) The first card Elizabeth turns over is a '4'. What is the chance of the 2nd card being lower than a 4?

A	B	C	D	E	F
Certain	Very Likely	Likely	Unlikely	Very Unlikely	Impossible

(1 mark)

(ii) The 2nd card Elizabeth picks up is a '2'. What is the chance of the 3rd card being higher?

A	B	C	D	E	F
Certain	Very Likely	Likely	Unlikely	Very Unlikely	Impossible

(1 mark)

(iii) The 3rd card Elizabeth picks up is an 'Ace'. What is the chance of the 4th card being higher?

A	B	C	D	E	F
Certain	Very Likely	Likely	Unlikely	Very Unlikely	Impossible

(1 mark)

15. (a) Michael wants to buy a new house.

The house he is looking at is currently £268,000.

The job market is set to drop its prices in the next month. Michael has a limit of £218,000.

By what percentage does the job market need to drop its price in order for Michael to be able to afford the house? To the nearest whole percentage.

....

....

....

....

....

....

(3 marks)

(b) In April, John earned £2,870. On his payslip, it shows that John was taxed £574.

(i) What percentage rate of tax did John pay?

....

....

....

(1 mark)

(ii) When John first started the job, he was told that his monthly earnings would be taxed by 18%.

Assuming this to be correct, and using (part i) to help, how much should John have earned after the correct amount of tax was taken?

....

....

....

(2 marks)

16. For the following questions, use the diagram below.

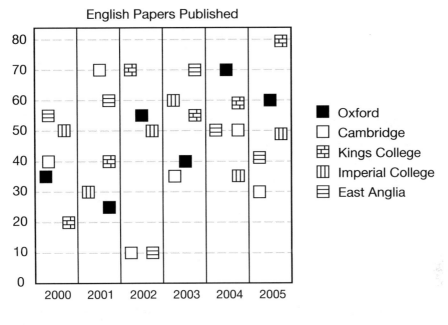

English Papers Published

Oxford
Cambridge
Kings College
Imperial College
East Anglia

(a) Which university/s published the second highest number of papers over the six year period?

....

....

(1 mark)

(b) In what year did researchers at Cambridge publish the most papers?

....

....

(1 mark)

(c) How many papers were published by Imperial College in 2004?

....

....

(1 mark)

(d) In what year did East Anglia College publish the lowest number of papers?

....

....

(1 mark)

(e) How many papers were published by Cambridge University over the six year period?

....

....

(1 mark)

17. Vincent is making biscuits for a fundraising event.

He has been using his grandma's special biscuit recipe which makes 25 biscuits.

Below is the recipe.

> ### Grandma's Special Biscuit Recipe
>
> | | |
> |---|---|
> | Self-raising flour | 210 grams |
> | Eggs | 2 |
> | Caster sugar | 110 grams |
> | Butter | 160 grams |
> | Blueberries | 60 grams |

In total, Vincent needs to bake 450 biscuits.

Work out how much of each ingredient Vincent is going to need.

....

....

....

....

....

Self-raising flour ....

Eggs ....

Caster sugar ....

Butter ....

Blueberries ....

(5 marks)

18. (a) What is the equation of the line?

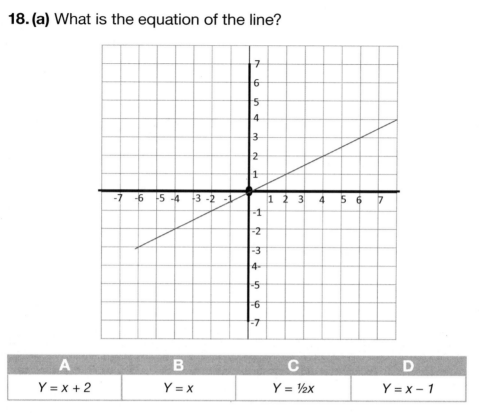

A	B	C	D
$Y = x + 2$	$Y = x$	$Y = \frac{1}{2}x$	$Y = x - 1$

(2 marks)

(b) Draw the line y = x + 3 on the graph below.

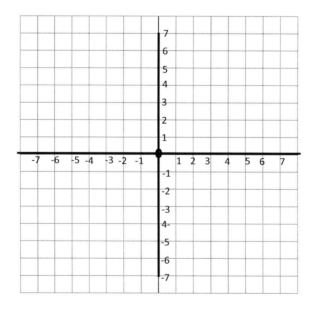

(3 marks)

19. Below is a net of a cuboid.

NOT DRAWN TO SCALE

```
              48 cm²

  36 cm²    108 cm²    36 cm²    108 cm²

              48 cm²
```

The net shows the **area** of each face of the cuboid.

Work out the **volume** of the cuboid.

....

....

....

....

....

....

....

....

....

Answer = ...

(5 marks)

20. The below diagram shows one square and four regular pentagons.

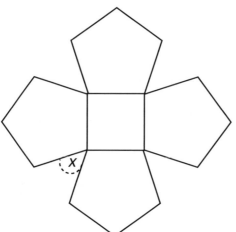

Work out the value of x.

....

....

....

Answer = ...

(2 marks)

21. Below is a table that lists the grades of 9 pupils.

Representation of the grades students achieved across five subjects

	English	Maths	Science	History	Media
David	A-	B+	C-	C+	B+
Billy	C-	C+	B+	A+	A
Elliott	B+	B-	A+	A-	C
Taralyn	C+	B+	B+	C+	A+
Alecia	C	C+	A-	B-	C+
James	B-	B+	C-	C+	C
Gareth	B+	B-	A	B-	C-
Duncan	B-	C-	C+	C-	C
Joe	B+	B	B	C	A

Grade	Pass Mark
A+	96-100
A	91-95
A-	86-90
B+	81-85
B	76-80
B-	71-75
C+	65-70
C	59-64
C-	50-58

(a) Work out the minimum possible of total marks across all nine candidates in Science.

....
....
....

Answer = ...

(1 mark)

(b) What is the highest mark across all five subjects that David could have got?

....
....
....

Answer = ...

(1 mark)

(c) What would Gareth's total average mark be, if he had scored the average mark in all his subjects?

....
....
....

Answer = ...

(1 mark)

GCSE Mathematics

SET A

Paper 2 Calculator

Higher Tier

1 hour and 45 minutes

INSTRUCTIONS TO CANDIDATES

- Use **black** ink.
- **Fill in the boxes** at the top of this page.
- Answer **all** of the questions.
- **Clearly** show your working outs.
- Take the value of π to be 3.142, or use the button π on your calculator.

INFORMATION FOR CANDIDATES

- The **total mark** for this paper is **100**.
- The marks for each question are shown on the **right** side of each page.
- Questions labelled with an asterisk (*) will assess the **quality** of **written communication**.

ADVICE FOR CANDIDATES

- Keep a close eye on the **time**.
- **Do not** spend too long on one question.
- Try to answer **every** question and show your workings out when required.

For examiner's use							
Q	Attempt No.			**Q**	Attempt No.		
	1	2	3		1	2	3
1				12			
2				13			
3				14			
4				15			
5				16			
6				17			
7				18			
8				19			
9				20			
10				21			
11							
TOTAL							

1. The Siberian tiger population in Country A is 60% of the Siberian tiger population in Country B. The population of Siberian tigers in Country C is 50% of that in the Country A.

   If the Siberian tiger population in Country C is 420, what is the Siberian tiger population in Country B?

   ....

   ....

   ....

   ....

   Answer = ...

   (2 marks)

2. **(a)** Write 8/26 as a decimal. To 3 significant figures.

   ....

   Answer = ...

   (1 mark)

   (b) Write 12/18 as a recurring decimal.

   ....

   Answer = ...

   (1 mark)

   (c) Write 62% as a fraction. Your answer should be written in its simplest form.

   ....

   Answer = ...

   (1 mark)

3. Below is a table which shows the number of times a die was cast, and the number of times it landed on each number.

The number of times a die was cast and the number of times each individual number appeared

Casts	1	2	3	4	5	6
First 10	2	3	1	1	2	1
First 20	5	4	3	4	3	1
First 30	8	5	6	5	4	2
First 40	10	6	7	6	5	6
First 50	13	7	10	7	6	7

(a) In no two consecutive casts did the same number appear. If the number 4 turned up in the 20th cast, which number/s could not have turned up in the 11th cast?

....

....

Answer = ...

(1 mark)

(b) Which number/s must have appeared the least amount of times in the first 50 casts?

....

....

Answer = ...

(1 mark)

(c) If the same number occurred for the 33rd cast and the 37th cast, what number/s could it be?

....

....

Answer = ...

(2 marks)

4. (a) Multiply out $(x - 10)^2$

....

....

Answer = ...

(1 mark)

(b) Multiply out $13a(2a - 5)$

....

....

Answer = ...

(1 mark)

(c) Expand and simplify $8(2a + 8) + 4(9a - 3)$

....

....

Answer = ...

(1 mark)

(d) Expand and simplify $9(x + 5) - 3(x - 8)$

....

....

Answer = ...

(1 mark)

(e) Factorise $63a^2 + 81b^2$

....

....

Answer = ...

(1 mark)

5. The two lines with arrows are parallel to one another.

NOT DRAWN TO SCALE

(a) (i) Work out the angle of x.

....

....

Answer = ...

(1 mark)

(ii) Give a reason for your answer.

....

....

(1 mark)

(b) (i) Work out angle Z.

....

....

Answer = ...

(1 mark)

(ii) Give a reason for your answer.

....

....

(1 marks)

6. Below shows a comparison of carbon emissions from last year to this year.

Carbon Emissions

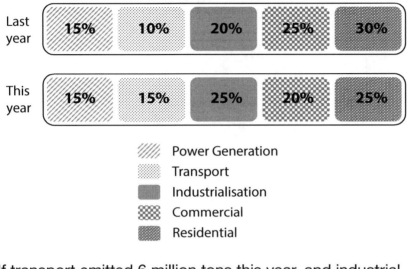

Last year   15%   10%   20%   25%   30%

This year   15%   15%   25%   20%   25%

░░░ Power Generation
░░░ Transport
▓▓▓ Industrialisation
▨▨▨ Commercial
▦▦▦ Residential

If transport emitted 6 million tons this year, and industrial emissions are the same as last year, what were the commercial emissions last year?

....
....
....
....
....
....
....
....
....
....

Answer = ...

(5 marks)

7. (a) Work out the length of side A. Give your answer correct to 1dp.

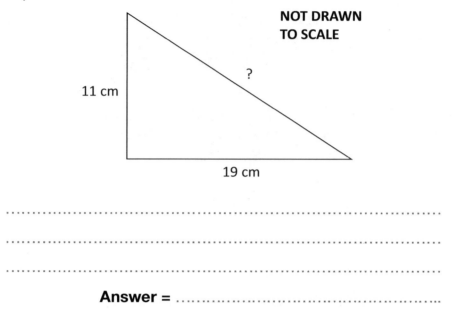

NOT DRAWN TO SCALE

11 cm

?

19 cm

Answer = ...

(2 marks)

(b) Work out angle X. Write your answer to 3 significant figures.

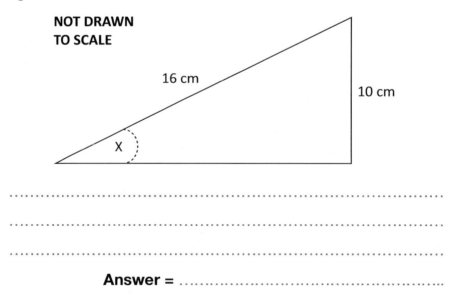

NOT DRAWN TO SCALE

16 cm

10 cm

X

Answer = ...

(2 marks)

(c) Work out the length of AB. Give your answer to 3 significant figures.

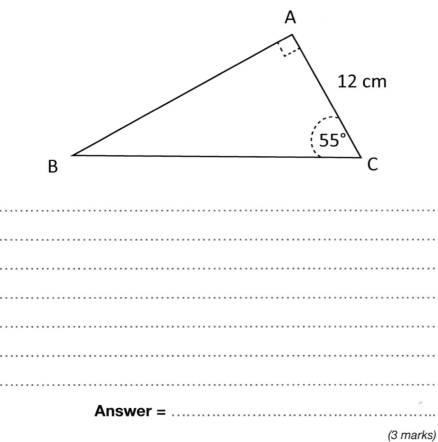

....

....

....

....

....

....

....

Answer = ...

(3 marks)

8. The diagram below shows the net of a square-based pyramid.

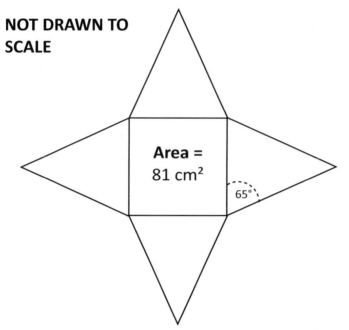

NOT DRAWN TO SCALE

Area = 81 cm²

65°

(a) If the height of the triangle is 8cm, work out the area of one of the triangles.

....

....

....

....

Answer = ...

(2 marks)

(b) Work out the total area of the whole shape.

....

....

....

Answer = ...

(3 marks)

9. (a) In July, Ryan worked a total of 40 hours.

In August he worked 46.5 hours.

By what percentage did Ryan's working hours increase in August?

....

....

....

Answer = ...

(2 marks)

(b) Below is a table which represents different companies, the cost to buy the company, and how much annual profit that company made.

Company	Company Profit (Annual) (£)	Cost to buy company (£)	Number of employees
A	15,000	18,000	6
B	26,000	24,000	11
C	22,000	20,000	8
D	40,000	40,000	10

If company D makes an annual profit of £15,000 the following year, what is the percentage decrease?

....

....

....

....

....

Answer = ...

(3 marks)

10. Samantha is a carpenter. She makes 3 oak tables for a family. The first table top measures 0.75 x 2 metres, the second measures 1.5 x 3 metres and the third measures 1.0 x 3 metres. What is the average area of the table tops?

....

....

....

....

Answer = ...

(3 marks)

11. (a) Using the diagram, calculate the perimeter of the lily bed.

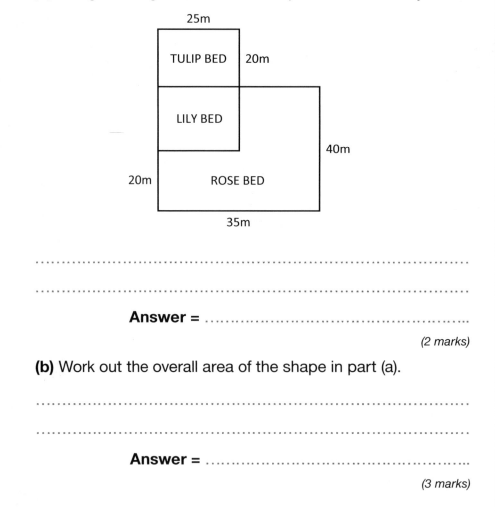

25m

TULIP BED   20m

LILY BED

40m

20m   ROSE BED

35m

....

....

Answer = ...

(2 marks)

(b) Work out the overall area of the shape in part (a).

....

....

Answer = ...

(3 marks)

12. Millie draws a triangle which has a base that is 7 cm longer than the height of the triangle. The area of the triangle is 85 cm². Work out the height of the triangle.

....

....

....

....

Answer = ...

(4 marks)

13. *C* is the centre of the circle.

Line *AB* is a tangent. From *Z* to *C* is a 90˚ angle.

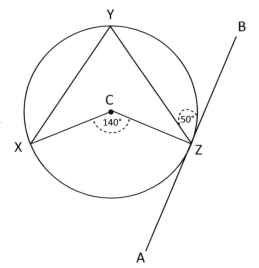

Work out the size of the angle *CXY*. You **must** show all of your working.

....

....

....

....

Answer = ...

(5 marks)

14. (a) An aircraft flying from London to Madrid is cruising at a speed of 534 mph.

The distance from departure is 500 miles and the time remaining to reach Madrid is 1 hour 10 minutes.

What is the total distance, in miles, from London to Madrid?

....

....

....

....

Answer = ...

(3 marks)

(b) On a flight from London to Rome, the following is shown on the information screen in the passenger cabin.

FLIGHT INFORMATION

Current speed = 822 km/hr

Distance from departure = 1222 km

Time to destination = 22 minutes

What is the distance, in kilometres, from London to Rome? Write your answer to the nearest kilometre.

....

....

....

....

Answer = ...

(3 marks)

15. The following table shows the daily earnings of an independent book publishing company.

Earnings (x)	Frequency
$500 \leq x < 540$	
$540 \leq x < 560$	
$560 \leq x < 570$	200
$570 \leq x < 600$	180
$600 \leq x < 640$	80
$640 \leq x < 700$	360

(a) Complete the above frequency table and draw the missing bars on the histogram below.

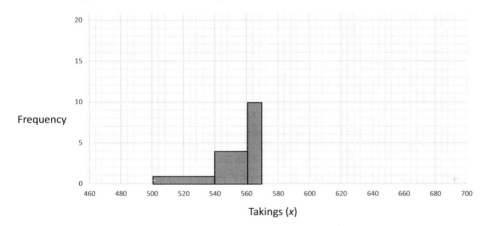

Takings (x)

(5 marks)

16. Work out this simultaneous equation:

$x + 2y = 22$

$-x + 5y = 27$

....

....

....

....

....

(4 marks)

17. The following graph shows the velocity of two cars at different times.

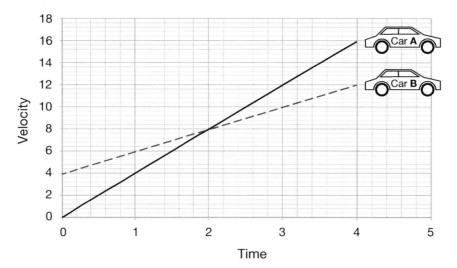

How much greater is the acceleration of Car A than the acceleration of Car B?

Acceleration (m/s2) = Change in velocity (m/s2) ÷ Change in time (s)

....

....

....

....

(3 marks)

18. (a) Using the graph below, plot the following inequalities.

$y = x$

$y = 4$

$y \le 8 - 4x$

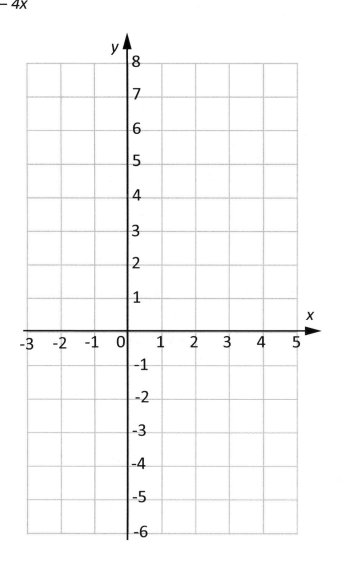

(3 marks)

(b) Using the graph above, shade in the region which satisfies all three inequalities.

(2 marks)

19. The table below is based on 100 students and their marks in English, Maths and Science examinations.

Marks out of 40				
Subject	30 and above	20 and above	10 and above	0 and above
English	19	52	91	100
Maths	13	36	90	100
Science	11	42	87	100
AVERAGE	11	43	89	100

(a) If at least 50% in their examination is needed to go on to higher education, how many students in Maths can go on to higher education?

....

....

Answer = ...

(2 marks)

(b) What is the percentage of students who achieved marks of 20 or above in their English exam?

....

....

....

Answer = ...

(2 marks)

(c) What is the difference between the number of students who achieved 30 or above in English and the number of students who achieved 20 and above in Science?

....

....

....

Answer = ...

(2 marks)

(d) Which subject had the most number of students who scored 10 or less?

....

....

....

Answer = ...

(2 marks)

20. Joe, David and Dan take it in turns driving from London to Dover, a total distance of approximately 80 miles per driver. Joe drives for 1 hour, David drives for 1 hour and 20 minutes, and Dan drives for 1 hour and 15 minutes.

(a) Calculate the average speed for Joe.

....

....

....

Answer = ...

(2 marks)

(b) Calculate the average speed for David.

....

....

....

Answer = ...

(2 marks)

(c) Calculate the average speed for Dan.

....

....

....

Answer = ...

(2 marks)

21. Here is a triangle made up of three sticks.

Pattern 1

The pattern continues as follows:

Pattern 1   Pattern 2   Pattern 3

(a) Work out how many sticks will be in the next four patterns.

Pattern 4	Pattern 5	Pattern 6	Pattern 7

(2 marks)

(b) If n represents the number of sticks, and p represents the pattern number, write a rule that can be applied in order to work out the next pattern in the sequence.

....

....

Answer = ...

(2 marks)

(c) Using your answer from (part b), work out how many sticks would be needed for the 118th pattern.

....

....

Answer = ...

(2 marks)

GCSE

Mathematics

SET A

Calculator and Non-Calculator Paper
Higher Tier

ANSWER BOOKLET

SET A – PAPER 1
(Non-Calculator)

1. 100

Estimations = 5,000 x 0.200 = 1,000

5.236 + 4.721 = 9.957 = 10

1,000 ÷ 10 = 100

3 marks

(2 marks for rounding the numbers up).

(1 mark for estimation being ± 10).

Q2. (a) (i) 4 x (12 ÷ 3) = 16 or (4 x 12) ÷ 3 = 16

1 mark

Q2. (a) (ii) 2 x (30 – 14) = 32

You need to subtract 30 by 14, before multiplying by 2.

1 mark

Q2 (a) (iii) Andy is correct. You need to do the multiplications before subtraction.

4 x 3 = 12

2 x 7 = 14

12 – 14 = -2

2 marks

(1 mark for correct answer).

(1 mark for explanation).

Q3. 11 m

12 + 6 + 2 = 20 metres is the total length.

Therefore 20 – 4 – 5 = 11 (you subtract the lengths you already know, in order to work out the missing length).

4 marks

(2 marks for correct answer).

(2 marks for showing working out).

Q4. (a) 5.24 x 10^5 Move the decimal point between the 5 and 7 = 5.24000 Count how many places the decimal point needs to be moved back to reach its original place = 5. So, 524,000 = 5.24 x 10^5	1 mark
Q4 (b) 8 x 10^{-6} 0.000008 = 8 x 0.000001 8 x 10^{-6}	2 marks (1 mark for correct answer). (1 mark for showing working out).
Q4 (c) 5.49686 x 10^7 55,000,000 – 31,400 54,968,600 = 5.49686 x 10^7	2 marks (1 mark for correct answer). (1 mark for showing working out).
Q5 (a) 14 out of 24 or 14/24 or 7/12. There are 8 orange counters. There are 6 pink counters. There are 24 counters in total. So, 8 + 6 = 14.	1 mark
Q5 (b) 16 out of 24 or 16/24 or 8/12 or 4/6 or 2/3. If Tessa does not want an orange counter, that means the probability of picking a colour she does want = 10 + 6 = 16 out of a total of 24.	1 mark
Q5 (c) ¼ Number of pink counters = 6 out of 24. 6/24 in its simplest form 1/4 (both numbers are divisible by 6).	1 mark

Q5 (d) 6 out of 30 or 6/30 or 1/5.

If 6 more counters are added, that means there are now 30 counters in total. Instead of 3 colours, the counters are now 5 different colours, which means there are 6 chances of picking a new colour.

1 mark

Q6. (a) The bar for (2-3 times) should reach 18. The bar for (5-6 times) should reach 30. The bar for (7-10 times) should reach 10.

2 marks
(2 marks for all correct bars. 1 mark for only two of the three bars drawn correctly).

Q6 (b) The first missing gap in the table should be 22. The second missing gap should be 30.

2 marks
(1 mark for each correct answer).

Q7 (a) 29 minutes

There are 8 people to perform self-evaluations for. There is a 10 minute interval between each = 70 minutes (1 hour and 10 minutes).

The self-evaluations need to be completed within 5 hours = 5 hours – 1 hour and 10 minutes = 3 hours and 50 minutes (230 minutes).

$230 \div 8 = 28.75$

To the nearest minute = 29.

3 marks
(1 mark for correct answer)
(1 mark for working out the minutes between each individual and subtracting it by the overall total).
(1 mark for dividing minutes by number of people).

Q7 (b) (i) £4189.50

$3,800 \div 100 \times 105 = 3990$
$3990 \div 100 \times 105 = 4189.50$

1 mark

Q7 (b) (ii) 6 years

$3,800 \div 100 \times 105 = 3990 = 1$ year
$3990 \div 100 \times 105 = 4189.5 = 2$ years
$4189 \div 100 \times 105 = 4398.45 = 3$ years
$4398 \div 100 \times 105 = 4617.90 = 4$ years
$4617 \div 100 \times 105 = 4847.85 = 5$ years
$4847 \div 100 \times 105 = 5089.35 = 6$ years

2 marks
(1 mark for correct answer).
(1 mark for working out each year).

Q8 (a) 122.4 0.5 x 3.1 x 48 + 48 = 122.4	3 marks (1 mark for correct answer). (1 mark for working out circumference). (1 mark for showing all working out with no more than one error).
Q8 (b) (i) 24.8 3.1 x 8 = 24.8	2 marks (1 mark for correct answer). (1 mark for showing correct formula for circumference of a circle).
Q8 (b) (ii) 49.6 3.1 x 4 x 4 = 49.6	2 marks (1 mark for correct answer). (1 mark for correct formula for area of a circle).
Q9 (a) $x = 72°$ 180 – 54 – 54 = 72	3 marks (1 mark for correct answer) (2 marks for showing workings out of other angles to reach angle x).
Q9 (b) $x = 19°$ Lines AB and CD are parallel. This means the angle of 19° is equivalent to angle x.	3 marks (1 mark for correct answer) (2 marks for showing workings out of other angles to reach angle x).
Q10 (a) (i) 120,000 centimetres 4 x 30,000 = 120,000	1 mark
Q10 (a) (ii) 1200 metres 120,000 ÷ 100 = 1200	1 mark
Q10 (a) (iii) 12 kilometres 1200 ÷ 100 = 12	1 mark

Q11 (a) (i) a = 5   and b = 1

$4a + 2b = 22$

$6a - 2b = 28$

Eliminate the b's

$10a = 50$

$a = 5$

$(4 \times 5) + 2b = 22$

$22 + (2 \times 1) = 22$

$b = 1$

2 marks

(1 mark for each correct answer).

Q11 (a) (ii) a = 4   and b = 5

$2a + 5b = 33$

$a + 3b = 19 \ (2a + 6b = 38)$

$2a + 5b = 33$

$2a + 6b = 38$

$b = 5$

$(5 \times 5) + 2a = 33$

$25 + 2a = 33$

$33 - 25 = 8 \ (8 \div 2 = 4)$

$a = 4$

2 marks

(1 mark for each correct answer).

Q11 (a) (iii) a = 3   and b = 2

$4a - 6b = 0 \ (\times 3)$

$6a + 2b = 22 \ (\times 2)$

$12a - 18b = 0$

$12a - 4b = 44$

$22b = 44$

$b = 2$

$4a - (6 \times 2) = 0$

$4a - 12 = 0$

$(4 \times 3) - 12 = 0$

$a = 3$

4 marks

(2 marks for each correct answer).

Q12. Your answer should look like this:

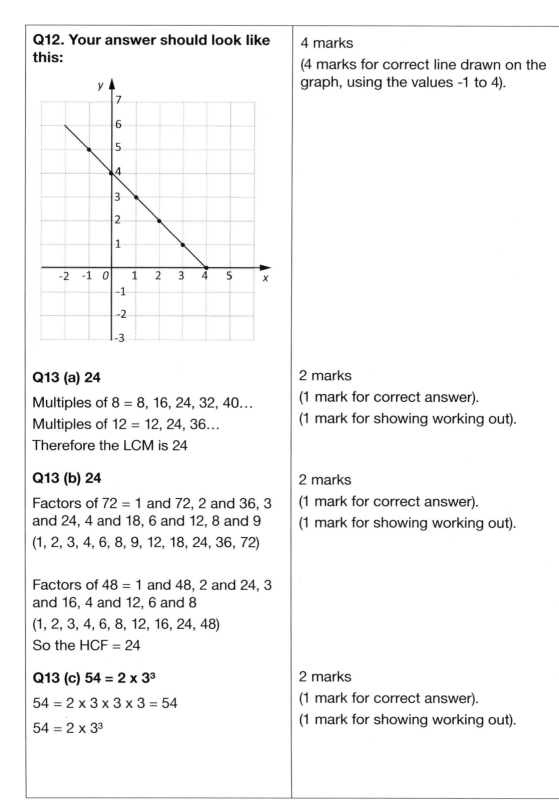

4 marks

(4 marks for correct line drawn on the graph, using the values -1 to 4).

Q13 (a) 24

Multiples of 8 = 8, 16, 24, 32, 40…

Multiples of 12 = 12, 24, 36…

Therefore the LCM is 24

2 marks

(1 mark for correct answer).

(1 mark for showing working out).

Q13 (b) 24

Factors of 72 = 1 and 72, 2 and 36, 3 and 24, 4 and 18, 6 and 12, 8 and 9

(1, 2, 3, 4, 6, 8, 9, 12, 18, 24, 36, 72)

Factors of 48 = 1 and 48, 2 and 24, 3 and 16, 4 and 12, 6 and 8

(1, 2, 3, 4, 6, 8, 12, 16, 24, 48)

So the HCF = 24

2 marks

(1 mark for correct answer).

(1 mark for showing working out).

Q13 (c) 54 = 2 x 3³

$54 = 2 \times 3 \times 3 \times 3 = 54$

$54 = 2 \times 3^3$

2 marks

(1 mark for correct answer).

(1 mark for showing working out).

Q14 (a) Your answer should look something like this:

Outcome	Number of ways to achieve this outcome	Total number of possible outcomes	Probability
Choosing a 'numbered' card	36	52	$^{36}/_{52}$ or $^{9}/_{13}$
Choosing a 'face' card	12	52	$^{12}/_{52}$
The card being between 5 and 9	20	52	$^{20}/_{52}$ or $^{5}/_{13}$

2 marks
(1 mark for each correct row).

Q14 (b) (i) Very unlikely

1 mark

Q14 (b) (ii) Very likely

1 mark

Q14 (b) (iii) Impossible

1 mark

Q15 (a) 19%

$268,000 - 218,000 = 50,000$

$50,000 \div 268,000 = 0.1865...$

$0.1865 \times 100 = 18.65\%$ decrease.

To the nearest whole percentage = 19%

3 marks
(1 mark for correct answer).
(1 mark for writing answer to the nearest whole number).
(1 mark for showing working out).

Q15 (b) (i) 20%

John was taxed 20%

He earned £2,870. He was taxed £574. So he took away = $2,870 - 574$ = 2296

$2,870 - 2296 = 574$
$574 \div 2870 = 0.2$
$0.2 \times 100 = 20\%$

1 mark

Q15 (b) (ii) £2353.40

$2,870 \div 100 = 28.7$

$28.7 \times 82 = 2353.40$

2 marks
(1 mark for correct answer).
(1 mark for showing working out).

Q16 (a) Oxford and East Anglia

1 mark

Q16 (b) 2001

1 mark

Q16 (c) 35

1 mark

Q16 (d) 2002	1 mark
Q16 (e) 235	1 mark
Q17. Self-raising flour = 3780 grams **Eggs = 36** **Caster sugar = 1980 grams** **Butter = 2880 grams** **Blueberries = 1080 grams** Self-raising flour = 210 ÷ 25 = 8.4 8.4 x 450 = 3780 grams Eggs = 36 Caster sugar = 110 ÷ 25 = 4.4 4.4 x 450 = 1980 grams Butter = 160 ÷ 25 = 6.4 6.4 x 450 = 2880 grams Blueberries = 60 ÷ 25 = 2.4 2.4 x 450 = 1080 grams	5 marks (1 mark for working out each ingredient).
Q18 (a) Y = ½x The value of x is half the value of y. When x is 4, y is 2.	2 marks
Q18 (b) Plot coordinates of (-3,0), (-2,1), (-1,2), (0,3) and so forth...	3 marks (3 marks for all correct plots drawn on the graph).
Q19. 432 108 cm = 12 x 9 48 cm = 12 x 4 36 cm = 9 x 4	5 marks (3 marks for working out the length, height and width). (1 mark for correct answer). (1 mark for showing working out with no more than one error).

Q20. 54°

Angles in a square = 90° (90 x 4 = 360°)

Angles in a regular pentagon = 108°

360 − 108 − 108 − 90 = 54°

2 marks

(1 mark for correct answer).

(1 mark for showing working out).

Q21 (a) 676

50 + 81 + 96 + 81 + 86 + 50 + 91 + 65 + 76 = 676

1 mark

Q21 (b) 388

90 + 85 + 58 + 70 + 85 = 388

1 mark

Q21 (c) 376

83 + 73 + 93 + 73 + 54 = 376

1 mark

SET A – PAPER 2
(Calculator)

Q1. 1,400 Siberian tiger population in Country C is 50% of that in Country A. If country C is 420, Country A = 420 x 100 ÷ 50 = 840. So, if Country A = 840 and is 60% of the population in Country B, Country B = 840 x 100 ÷ 60 = 1,400.	2 marks (1 mark for correct answer). (1 mark for showing working out).
Q2 (a) 0.31 8 ÷ 26 = 0.30769… To 3 significant figures = 0.31	1 mark
Q2 (b) 0.6666 12 ÷ 18 = 0.666666….	1 mark
Q2 (c) 31/50 62% = 62/100 = 31/50 Both numbers can be divided by 2.	1 mark
Q3 (a) 6 The question may seem tricky at first, but if you notice, the individual number of 6 was cast once in the first 10 attempts, and only once in the first 20 attempts. Therefore, the number 6 could not have turned up from casts 11 – 20.	1 mark

Q3 (b) 5   1 mark

The number 5 only appears 6 times in the first 50 casts, no other number has a lower cast rate at the end of 50 casts, and therefore 5 is the number with the least amount of casts in 50 attempts.

Q3 (c) 1 and 6   2 marks

The numbers have to occur more than once between 30 and 40. Only the numbers 1 and 6 do this, therefore this would be the correct answer.

Q4 (a) x^2 - 20x + 100   1 mark

X times $X = X^2$

X times -10 = -10x

-10 times X = -10x

-10 times -10 = 100

The expression looks like this: x^2 - 10x − 10x + 100

x^2 - 20x + 100

Q4 (b) $26a^2$ - 65a   1 mark

13a x 2a = $26a^2$

13a x -5 = -65a

$26a^2$ − 65a

Q4 (c) 52a + 52   1 mark

8(2a + 8) + 4(9a − 3)

16a + 64 + 36a − 12

52a + 52

Q4 (d) 6x + 69   1 mark

9(x + 5) − 3(x − 8)

9x + 45 − 3x + 24

6x + 69

Q4 (e) 9(7a² + 9b²)

The highest common factor is 9, so this will go outside the brackets. Use this number to work out what you need to multiply to get the expression.

1 mark

Q5 (a) (i) x = 78°

1 mark

Q5 (a) (ii) Corresponding to the angle 78°

Angle x is on a parallel line, which means it will be the same value as 78°.

1 mark

Q5 (b) (i) z = 72°

180 − 108 = 72°

1 mark

Q5 (b) (ii) The angles of a straight line add up to 180°. Angle z is equivalent to the angle that is opposite to the 180°.

1 mark

Q6. 12.5 million tons

If transport emissions this year are 6 million tons – and equal 15% of the total – the overall total for this year would be 6,000,000 x 100 ÷ 15% = 40,000,000.

So industrial emissions for this year would be = 40,000,000 ÷ 100 x 25 = 10,000,000.

The industrial emissions are the same for last year, so to work out the overall total of last year = 10,000,000 x 100 ÷ 20 = 50,000,000.

So the commercial emissions for last year = 50,000,000 ÷ 100 x 25 = 12,500,000 (12.5 million tons).

5 marks

(1 mark for correct answer).

(2 marks for working out totals for this year).

(2 marks for working out totals for last year).

Q7 (a) 22 cm

$11^2 = 121$

$19^2 = 361$

$121 + 361 = 482$

$\sqrt{482} = 21.95449\ldots$

To one decimal place = 22.0

2 marks

(1 mark for correct answer).

(1 mark for showing working out).

Q7 (b) Angle X = 38.7°

Sin X = 10⁄16 0.625

Inv Sin = 38.6821…

To 3 significant figures = 38.7

2 marks

(1 mark for correct answer).

(1 mark for showing working out).

Q7 (c) AB = 17.1 cm

tan 55 = AB⁄12

12 x tan 55 = 17.137

To 3 significant figures = 17.1 cm

3 marks

(1 mark for correct answer).

(2 marks for showing working out with no more than one error).

Q8 (a) 36 cm²

9 x 8 – 72

72 ÷ 2 = 36

2 marks

(1 mark for correct answer).

(1 mark for showing working out).

Q8 (b) 225 cm²

36 x 4 = 144

144 + 81 = 225

3 marks

(1 mark for correct answer).

(2 marks for showing working out).

Q9 (a) 16.25%

To tackle this problem first we calculate the difference in hours between the new and old numbers. 46.5 - 40 hours = 6.5 hours. We can see that Ryan worked 6.5 hours more in August than he did in July – this is his increase.

To work out the increase as a percentage it is now necessary to divide the increase by the original (January) number: 6.5 ÷ 40 = 0.1625

Finally, to get the percentage we

2 marks

(1 mark for correct answer).

(1 mark for showing working out).

multiply the answer by 100. This simply means moving the decimal place two columns to the right.

$0.1625 \times 100 = 16.25$.

Ryan therefore worked 16.25% more hours in August than he did in July.

Q9 (b) 62.5%

EXPLANATION = 40,000 – 15,000 = 25,000.

So, 25,000 ÷ 40,000 x 100 = 62.5%.

3 marks
(1 mark for correct answer).
(2 marks for working out).

Q10. 3 metres²

3 marks
(1 mark for correct answer).
(2 marks for working out with no more than one error).

Q11 (a) 90 metres

Perimeter of lily bed = 25 + 25 + 20 + 20 = 90

2 marks
(1 mark for correct answer).
(1 mark for working out with no more than one error).

Q11 (b) Area = 1900 cm²

25 x 20 = 500

40 x 35 = 1400

1400 + 500 = 1900 cm²

3 marks
(1 mark for correct answer).
(2 marks for working out with no more than one error).

Q12. 10 cm

17 (base) x 10 (height) = 170

170 ÷ 2 = 85

4 marks
(1 mark for correct answer).
(3 marks for working out with no error. Deduct one mark for each error).

Q13. 50°

$180 - 40 - 90 = 50$

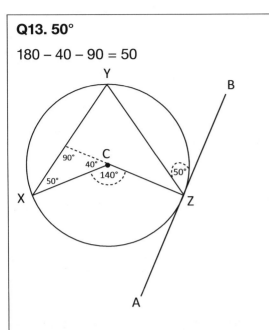

5 marks

(1 mark for correct answer).

(4 marks for working out with no error. Deduct one mark for each error).

Q14 (a) 1,123 miles

500 miles have already been covered by the aircraft. The speed is 534 mph and the time of flight remaining is 1 hour 10 minutes = 70 minutes = 70/60 hours.

Distance remaining = speed x time remaining

$534 \times (70 \div 60)$

623 miles.

The distance from London to Madrid is 623 + 500 = 1,123 miles.

3 marks

(1 mark for correct answer).

(1 mark for finding the distance remaining).

(1 mark for adding the distance from London to Madrid).

Q14 (b) 1,423 kilometres

1222 km has already been covered

Distance remaining = speed x time remaining

Speed = 822 km/hr

Time = 22m = 22/60 hours

Remaining distance = speed x time

$822 \times [22/60]$ km = 301.4 km

3 marks

(1 mark for correct answer).

(1 mark for finding the distance remaining).

(1 mark for working out the distance between London and Rome).

Total distance between London and Rome, in km = 1222 + 301.4 = 1,523.4

Whole kilometres = 1,523

Q15 (a) The two missing gaps in the table are 40 and 80.

The bar for 560-600 = frequency of 6.

The bar for 600-640 = frequency of 2.

The bar for 640-700 = frequency of 9.

Remember = frequency = frequency density ÷ class width

Frequency density = frequency ÷ class width

5 marks

(2 marks for filling the gaps in the table correctly).

(3 marks to be awarded for drawing all 4 correct bars. 2 marks for 3 correct bars. 1 mark for 2 correct bars).

Q16. x = 8 and y = 7

$x + 2y = 22$

$-x + 5y = 27$

$7y = 49$

$y = 7$

$(2 \times 7) + x = 22$

$14 + x = 22$

$x = 8$

4 marks

(2 marks for working out the value of x. No errors in working out).

(2 marks for working out the value of y. No errors in working out).

Q17. 2 m/s2

(y final – y initial) ÷ (x final – x initial).

Car A = (16-0) ÷ (4-0) = 16 ÷ 4 = 4.

Car B = (12-4) ÷ (4-0) = 8 ÷ 4 = 2.

So, the difference between car A and car B is 2 m/s2.

3 marks

(1 mark for correct answer).

(1 mark for working out Car A).

(1 mark for working out Car B).

Q18 (a) Your answer should look like this:

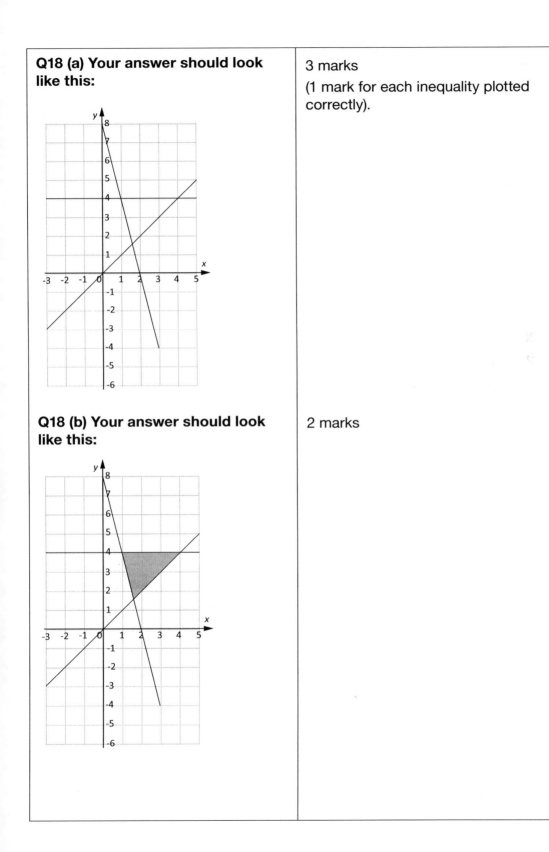

3 marks

(1 mark for each inequality plotted correctly).

Q18 (b) Your answer should look like this:

2 marks

Q19 (a) 36

50% of 40 = 20. Number of students who scored 20 and above in Maths = 36.

2 marks

(1 mark for correct answer).

(1 mark for showing working out).

Q19 (b) 52%

100 students, 52 students achieved marks of 20 or above = 52%.

2 marks

(1 mark for correct answer).

(1 mark for showing working out).

Q19 (c) 23

Number of students with 30 or above in English = 19. Students with 20 or above in Science = 42.
So 42 -19 = 23.

2 marks

(1 mark for correct answer).

(1 mark for showing working out).

Q19 (d) Science

Science had 13 people who scored less than 10. Therefore Science is the subject that has the most number of people who scored less than 10.

2 marks

(1 mark for correct answer).

(1 mark for showing working out).

Q20 (a) 80 mph

Average speed for Joe

Joe drives 80 miles in 1 hour. Therefore Joe completed his drive at a speed of 80 miles per hour.

2 marks

(1 mark for correct answer).

(1 mark for showing working out).

Q20 (b) 60 mph

Average speed for David

David drives 80 miles in 1 hour and 20 minutes 60/80 = 0.75

0.75 x 80 (miles) = 60 mph

2 marks

(1 mark for correct answer).

(1 mark for showing working out).

Q20 (c) 64 mph

Average speed for Dan

Dan drives 80 miles in 1 hour and 15 minutes

60/75 = 0.8

0.8 x 80 = 64 mph

2 marks

(1 mark for correct answer).

(1 mark for showing working out).

Q21 (a) Pattern 4 = 9, Pattern 5 = 11, Pattern 6 = 13, Pattern 7 = 15

Add two sticks to the previous pattern.

2 marks

(1 mark for every 2 correct answers).

Q21 (b) number of sticks *(n)* = pattern number *(p)* x 2 + 1

To progress in this sequence, you need to multiply the pattern number by 3, and then add 1.

2 marks

(1 mark for correct answer).

(1 mark for showing working out).

Q21 (c) 237

Number of sticks = pattern number x 2 + 1

118 x 2 = 236 + 1 = 237

2 marks

(1 mark for correct answer).

(1 mark for showing working out).

GCSE Mathematics

SET B
Paper 1 Non-Calculator

Higher Tier

1 hour and 45 minutes

INSTRUCTIONS TO CANDIDATES

- Use **black** ink.
- **Fill in the boxes** at the top of this page.
- Answer **all** of the questions.
- **Clearly** show your working outs.

INFORMATION FOR CANDIDATES

- The **total mark** for this paper is **100**.
- The marks for each question are shown on the **right** side of each page.
- Questions labelled with an asterisk (*) will assess the **quality** of **written communication**.

ADVICE FOR CANDIDATES

- Keep a close eye on the **time**.
- **Do not** spend too long on one question.
- Try to answer **every** question and show your workings out when required.

Q	Attempt No.			Q	Attempt No.		
	1	2	3		1	2	3
For examiner's use (title spanning full table)							

For examiner's use

Q	Attempt No. 1	2	3	Q	Attempt No. 1	2	3
1				12			
2				13			
3				14			
4				15			
5				16			
6				17			
7				18			
8				19			
9				20			
10				21			
11							
TOTAL							

GCSE Mathematics

Higher Tier

Formula Sheet

Volume of cone $= \frac{1}{3}\pi r^2 h$

Curved surface area of cone $= \pi r l$

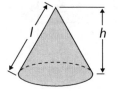

Volume of sphere $= \frac{4}{3}\pi r^3$

Surface area of sphere $= 4\pi r^2$

Volume of prism = area of cross section x length

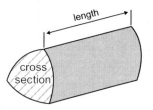

In any triangle *ABC*

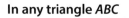
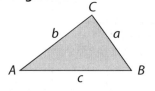

The Quadratic Equation

The solutions of $ax^2 + bx + c = 0$ where $a \neq 0$, are given by

$$x = \frac{-b \pm \sqrt{(b^2 - 4ac)}}{2a}$$

Sine Rule $\dfrac{a}{\sin A} = \dfrac{b}{\sin B} = \dfrac{c}{\sin C}$

Cosine Rule $a^2 = b^2 + c^2 - 2bc \cos A$

Area of triangle $= \frac{1}{2} ab \sin C$

1. L-shape *Y* is an enlargement of L-shape *X*.

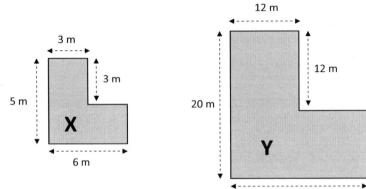

NOT DRAWN TO SCALE

(a) Work out the scale factor of the enlargement.

....

Answer = ...

(1 mark)

(b) Enlarge the shape using a scale factor of 3.

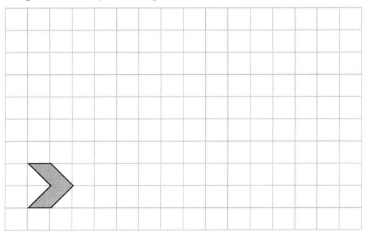

(2 marks)

2. (a) Estimate the answer to:

$$\frac{12.7 \times 30.2}{2.7}$$

You **must** show all of your working.

....

....

....

Answer = ...

(2 marks)

(b) (i) Work out the following:

$4\frac{2}{3} + 3\frac{1}{4}$. Write your answer as a mixed number.

....

....

....

Answer = ...

(2 marks)

(ii) Work out the following:

$7\frac{3}{4} \div 3\frac{2}{3}$. Write your answer as a mixed number.

....

....

....

Answer = ...

(2 marks)

3. (a) Find the missing side length of the triangle. Write your answer to 1 dp.

NOT DRAWN TO SCALE

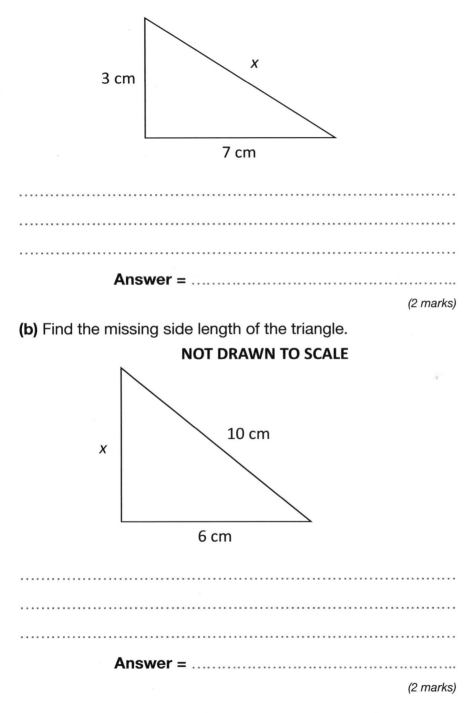

3 cm

x

7 cm

....

....

....

Answer = ...

(2 marks)

(b) Find the missing side length of the triangle.

NOT DRAWN TO SCALE

10 cm

x

6 cm

....

....

....

Answer = ...

(2 marks)

4. The following table shows the prices of a travel agents holiday prices for booking holidays for next year.

HOLIDAY PRICES				
Types of Holiday Deals	Turkey	Mexico	America	Spain
All inclusive	£276pp	£720pp	£880pp	£320pp
Half board	£220pp	£640pp	£795pp	£275pp
Self-Catering	£180pp	£550pp	£620pp	£235pp

How much more would it cost if three all-inclusive holidays each for two people to Mexico were booked, as opposed to one booking for a self-catering holiday to Turkey for five people?

....

....

Answer = ...

(3 marks)

5. (a) Expand $y(y - 10)$

....

....

Answer = ...

(1 mark)

(b) Simplify $20x^2 - 8a - 3x^2 + 4a - x$

....

....

Answer = ...

(2 marks)

(c) Factorise $18x^2 - 12$

....

....

Answer = ...

(2 marks)

(d) Make x the subject of the formula $ax = 2y + 2z$

....

....

....

Answer = ...

(2 marks)

6. Andy is decorating his home. He is working on his kitchen and bathroom.

Two walls in the bathroom and two walls in the kitchen need tiling. The layout of these walls for both the kitchen and bathroom are shown below. The diagrams illustrate the walls from a front point of view.

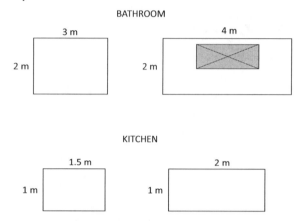

One of the walls in the bathroom has a window, so you will need to tile around that. The window is 1 metre in length and 0.5 metres in height.

(a) Work out the total area for the bathroom and kitchen that needs tiling.

....

....

Answer = ...

(2 marks)

(b) Each tile is 25 cm in length and 10cm in height. How many tiles are needed to complete this tiling job?

....

....

....

....

Answer = ...

(3 marks)

7. The below diagram shows a prism.

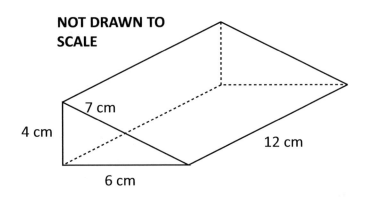

NOT DRAWN TO SCALE

7 cm

4 cm

6 cm

12 cm

(a) Work out the volume of the prism. You **must** show all your working.

....

....

....

....

Answer = ...

(3 marks)

(b) How many of these trianglular prisms would you need, in order to make up a cuboid with a height of 80 cm, but the width and length still being the same as (part a)?

....

....

....

....

Answer = ...

(3 marks)

8. The diagram below shows a parallelogram.

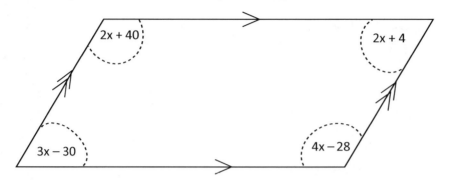

The angles in the parallelogram are as follows:

2x + 40

3x − 30

2x + 4

4x − 28

Work out the value of x.

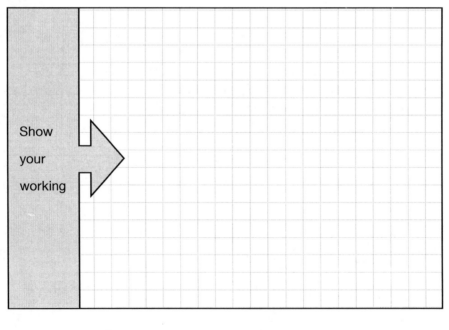

Show
your
working

Answer = ...

(4 marks)

9. For each of the expressions below, work out the value. Your answer should be given in standard form.

(a) $10^{100} \times 4 \times 3 \times 10^{400}$

....

....

Answer = ...

(2 marks)

(b) Write 856,000 in standard form.

....

....

Answer = ...

(2 marks)

(c) Write 0.00485 in standard form.

....

....

Answer = ...

(2 marks)

10. Here are five cards, each with its own number.

| 8 | 9 | 3 | 0 | 7 |

(a) The above number reads 89,307. Write this number in words.

....

....

....

(1 mark)

(b) (i) Write the above number to the nearest **10**.

....

(1 mark)

(ii) Write the above number to the nearest **100**.

....

(1 mark)

(iii) Write the above number to the nearest **1,000**.

....

(1 mark)

11. A science class is working on acceleration and velocity.

Below shows a velocity-time graph which a student has drawn to represent the acceleration of an object.

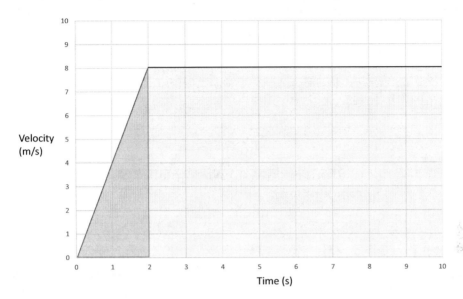

(a) Using the sloping line of the velocity-time graph, what is the acceleration?

....

....

Answer = ...

(2 marks)

(b) Assuming the object continues to maintain its acceleration at the same rate of speed, how many seconds will it take the object to have a velocity of 64?

....

....

....

Answer = ...

(3 marks)

12. An English class of 16 have just sat a mock Exam.

The exam has 2 sections – Literature and Language. It takes approximately 6 minutes to mark the Literature section and 7 minutes to mark the Language section.

A Science class have also taken a mock exam, which 14 students completed.

The exam comprises of three sections, each of which will take 10 minutes to mark.

2 minutes is given for each exam, to double check the marking.

How long in hours and minutes does it take to mark the English and Science mock exams?

....

....

....

....

....

....

Answer = ...

(4 marks)

13. Below is a map showing different storage lock ups.

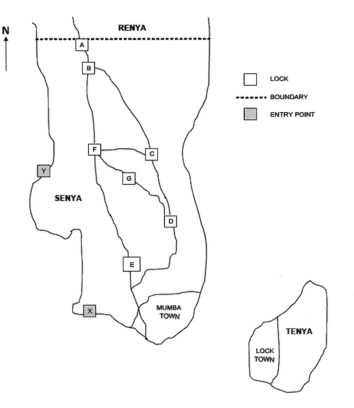

(a) Using a protractor, work out the bearing from lock-up C to lock-up Y.

....

....

Answer = ...

(3 marks)

(b) If the scale of the map is 1cm = 5km, work out the distance, using a straight line, between lock-up A and lock-up X.

....

....

Answer = ...

(3 marks)

14. Using the calculation that 34 x 3245 = 110,330, calculate the following:

(a) 34 x 32.45

....

....

Answer = ...

(1 mark)

(b) 110,330 ÷ 340

....

....

Answer = ...

(1 mark)

(c) 3.4 x 3.245

....

....

Answer = ...

(1 mark)

(d) 110,330 ÷ 3.4

....

....

Answer = ...

(1 mark)

(e) 0.34 x 324.5

....

....

Answer = ...

(1 mark)

15. A two-stage operation flow diagram is shown below.

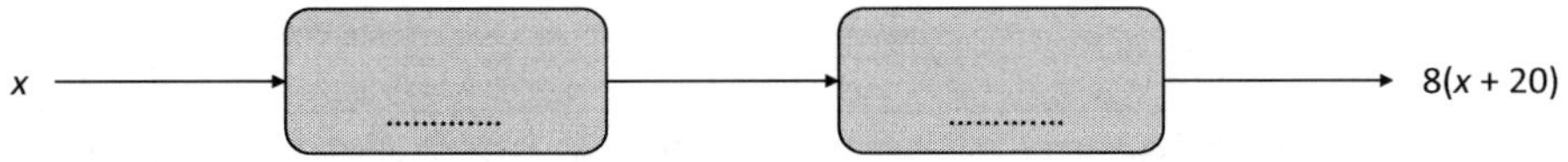

x ⟶ [.............] ⟶ [.............] ⟶ $8(x + 20)$

(a) Fill in the diagram above, in order to show which operations are needed to complete the flow diagram.

(2 marks)

(b) Using your operations from (part a), if the input was -4, what is the output of the machine.

....

....

Answer = ...

(2 marks)

16. Imogen wants to buy a large corner sofa, a foot stool and an arm chair.

She is looking for the best prices.

She browses on the internet, and has narrowed it down to three possibilities.

Store A

Large corner sofa: £420

A foot stool = £33.50

Arm chair = £112

+ £12.50 for postage

Store B

Large corner sofa: £550

A foot stool = £20

Arm chair = £84.90

Free postage

Store C

Large corner sofa: £320

A foot stool = £20.99

Arm chair = £80

+ £13.00 for postage

Which store offers the best price? You must show your working out.

....

....

....

....

....

....

....

....

....

....

Answer = ...

(3 marks)

17. Here is an equation:　　$y = 2x + 2$

(a) Complete the table below using the equation above.

x	-2	-1	0	1	2	3
y				4	6	

(2 marks)

(b) On the grid below, draw a line that represents the equation　　$y = 2x + 2$

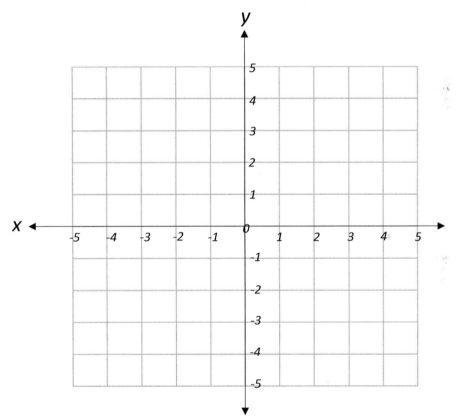

(3 marks)

18. Below is a set of scores listed for 30 people. These scores are out of 100 and are for a general knowledge pop quiz.

13	68	39	68	79
12	57	29	67	84
94	35	38	31	30
11	69	85	37	19
38	40	90	80	50
55	65	63	73	78

(a) Using the information above, fill in the stem and leaf diagram below.

KEY:

(3 marks)

(b) What is the median score in the general knowledge pop quiz?

....

....

Answer = ...

(1 mark)

(c) What is the mean score in the general knowledge pop quiz? To the nearest whole number.

....

....

Answer = ...

(1 mark)

(d) What is the range in the general knowledge pop quiz?

....

....

Answer = ...

(1 mark)

(e) What is the percentage of people who scored 60 or more in the general knowledge pop quiz? To the nearest whole number.

....

....

Answer = ...

(1 mark)

19. Below shows two tourist locations, Sandy Beach and Joy Town.

Joy Town

Sandy Beach

(a) The airport is on a bearing of 045°, 20 kilometres away from Sandy Beach. *5 kilometres = 2cm.*

Mark the position of the airport using the correct bearing and scale.

(1 mark)

(b) From Joy Town, a tourist wants to visit the Zoo. This is on a bearing 215°. This is 10 kilometres away from Sandy Beach.

Mark the position of the Zoo using the correct bearing and scale.

(2 marks)

20. Fiona has recorded results, in minutes, in which girls from her class took to complete a brain teaser.

	Minutes
Shortest time	16
Lower quartile	20
Median	28
Upper quartile	46
Longest time	52

(a) Use the above information, and create a box plot diagram to represent the times in which it took girls in Fiona's class to complete a brain teaser.

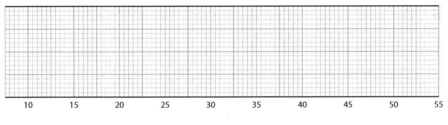

(2 marks)

(b) Below is a box plot diagram showing the times it took boys to complete the brain teaser. Write down one comparison between girls and boys times.

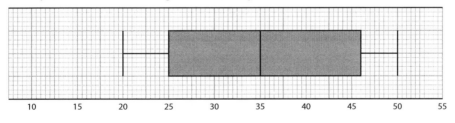

Compare the differences between the girls' times and the boys' times.

....

....

....

(2 marks)

21. (a) Henry and Jordan are having a debate about algebra.

Jordan says:

"When you add two consecutive numbers, the total will always be odd".

Henry disputes this.

Using algebra and examples, show how Jordan's statement is **true**.

....

....

....

....

....

....

....

(3 marks)

(b) Gemma joins in the conversation with Henry and Jordan.

She would like to point out an interesting fact about algebra:

"If three consecutive numbers are added together, the sum of all three numbers will always be divisible by 3".

Using algebra and examples, work out whether or not Gemma is correct.

....

....

....

....

....

....

....

(3 marks)

GCSE Mathematics

SET B
Paper 2 Calculator

Higher Tier
1 hour and 45 minutes

INSTRUCTIONS TO CANDIDATES

- Use **black** ink.
- **Fill in the boxes** at the top of this page.
- Answer **all** of the questions.
- **Clearly** show your working outs.
- Take the value of π to be 3.142, or use the button π on your calculator.

INFORMATION FOR CANDIDATES

- The **total mark** for this paper is **100**.
- The marks for each question are shown on the **right** side of each page.
- Questions labelled with an asterisk (*) will assess the **quality** of **written communication**.

ADVICE FOR CANDIDATES

- Keep a close eye on the **time**.
- **Do not** spend too long on one question.
- Try to answer **every** question and show your workings out when required.

Q	Attempt No.			Q	Attempt No.		
	1	2	3		1	2	3
1				12			
2				13			
3				14			
4				15			
5				16			
6				17			
7				18			
8				19			
9				20			
10				21			
11							
TOTAL							

For examiner's use

Answer ALL questions.
Write your answers in the spaces provided.

1. **(a)** William is teaching his friend Daniel how to work out the nth term in a sequence.

   William uses the following sequence as his example:

   n^{th} term $= 9n - 3$

   Work out the first 6 terms using the above sequence.

1st term	2nd term	3rd term	4th term	5th term	6th term

(2 marks)

   (b) William uses another example, but instead of giving Daniel the sequence, he gives him the rule:

   "Double the previous term and add 5".

   (i) If the 3rd term in this sequence is 27, what is the first term?

   ....

   Answer = ...

(2 marks)

   (ii) Using the same rule, what would 4th, 5th, 6th and 7th term be in the sequence?

   ....

   ....

   Answer = ...

(1 mark)

2. Below shows three graphs.

For each of the graphs, write the correct equation to represent the line.

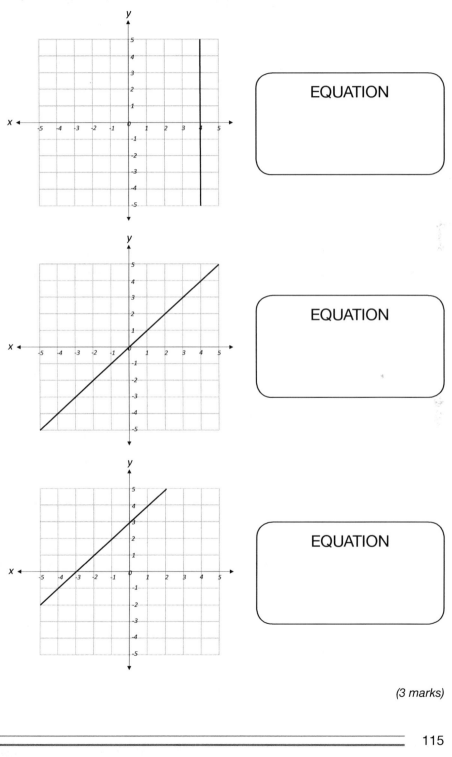

EQUATION

EQUATION

EQUATION

3. The table below has recorded students' favourite sport in P.E. The results are as follows:

Sport	Frequency
Football	31
Tennis	24
Rounders	16
Dance	15
Hockey	4

Using the above information, accurately complete the pie chart.

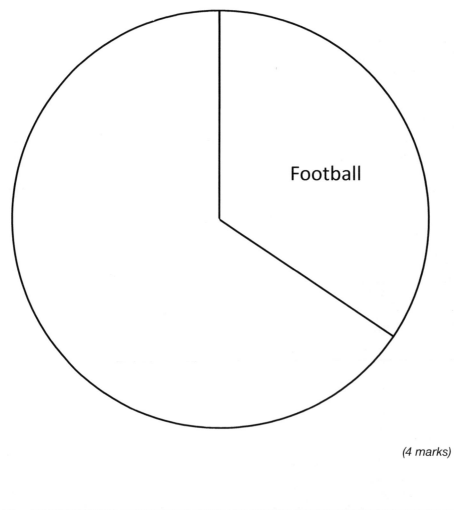

(4 marks)

4. Sarah draws two shapes – a square and a circle. The area of the square is 49 cm².

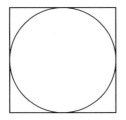

She then makes a pattern using the two shapes which looks like this:

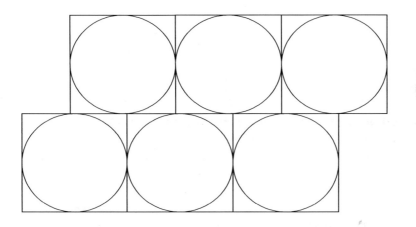

Work out the total surface area which is covered by circles. All calculations should be rounded to 2 decimal places.

....

....

....

....

....

....

....

Answer = ...

(5 marks)

5. This week, Mark has three sets of homework to complete – English, Maths and Science.

Mark spends ¼ of his time completing his Science homework. He spends 10% of his time completing his Maths homework.

(a) Work out the amount of time Mark spends on his English homework. Give your answer as a decimal.

....

....

Answer = ...

(1 mark)

(b) The following week, Mark has no Science homework but still has English and Maths. Instead of his Science homework, he has two mini tests to complete. He decides to split his time that he usually spends on Science, equally between the two tests. He keeps the same proportions for English and Maths.

If Mark spends 2 hours in total, work out how long he spends on his English homework, Maths homework and each mini test.

....

....

....

....

....

English = ...

Maths = ...

Mini test 1 = ...

Mini test 2 = ...

(2 marks)

6. The diagram below shows a right-angle triangle.

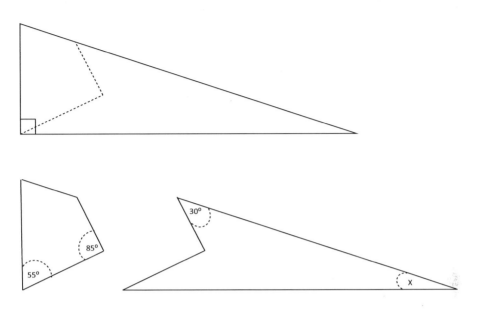

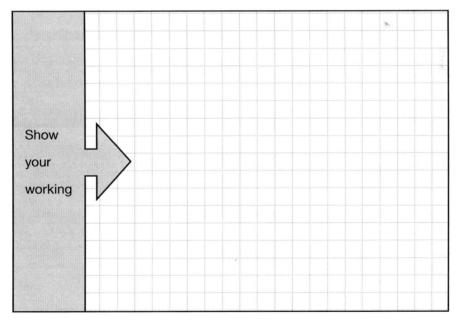

The triangle is cut along the dotted line below, producing two new shapes.

Work out the value of X. You **must** show all of your working.

Show
your
working

(4 marks)

7. Use trial and improvement to find the solution of:

$$x^3 - 4x = 10$$

Give your answer to 1 decimal place.

x	$x^3 - 4x = 10$	Too small? Too big?
2	$2^3 - 4 \times 2 = 0$	Too small

(4 marks)

8. Below is a table listing the percentage changes from 2012 to 2014 for five different companies.

COMPANY	Percentage Change from 2012-2013	Percentage Change from 2013-2014
Company A	+17%	-5%
Company B	+12%	+5%
Company C	-11%	+8%
Company D	-5%	-7%
Company E	+8%	-3%

(a) Using the above table, if company B earned £412,500 in 2012, how much money did the company make in 2014?

....

....

....

Answer = ...

(2 marks)

(b) If Company C earned £765,085 in 2012, what was the difference between earnings from that year to the next?

....

....

....

Answer = ...

(2 marks)

9. A bank pays 6.8% **compound** interest per year on an investment of £7000.

   How many years will it take the investment to reach over £10,000? For each year, the total should just be of whole pounds.

   ....

   ....

   ....

   ....

   ....

   ....

   ....

   ....

   Answer = ...

   (3 marks)

10. The Earth travels around the sun once a year.

    The average distance of the earth from the sun is 1.5×10^{11} m.

    Work out the distance between the earth and the sun. Write your answer in kilometres.

    ....

    ....

    ....

    ....

    ....

    ....

    ....

    ....

    Answer = ...

    (4 marks)

11. *(a)** Work out which of the following has a greater value:

20 (15 ÷ 3) + (4^3 x 5^2)

Or

$\sqrt{1600}$ x 50 – 72

Explain your answer.

....

....

....

....

....

(3 marks)

*(b)** Lena has taken a loan out from her bank. She borrows £1,600 which has a rate of 25% compound interest added per year.

Lena has calculated that she will be able to pay off her loan in 4 years.

Explain how you know that Lena will be paying off over double the amount she borrowed originally.

....

....

....

....

....

....

(3 marks)

12. Below is a velocity-time graph.

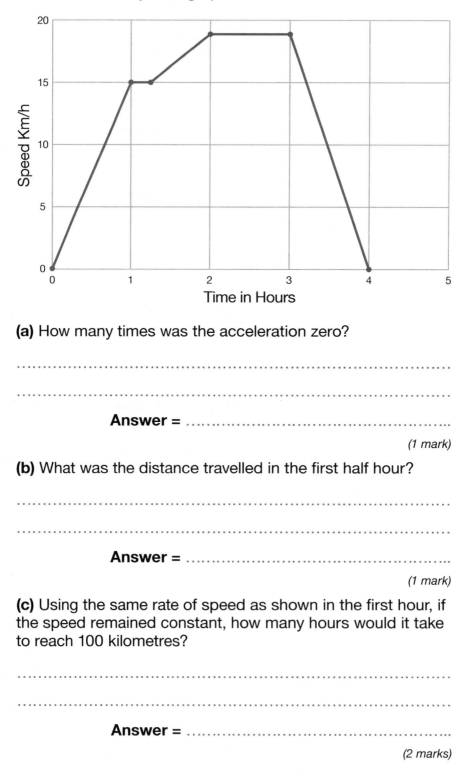

Time in Hours

(a) How many times was the acceleration zero?

....

....

Answer = ...

(1 mark)

(b) What was the distance travelled in the first half hour?

....

....

Answer = ...

(1 mark)

(c) Using the same rate of speed as shown in the first hour, if the speed remained constant, how many hours would it take to reach 100 kilometres?

....

....

Answer = ...

(2 marks)

13. Government spending on 'Education services' was 56.3 billion pounds.

Government spending on 'Health services' was 106.7 billion.

In the same year, the Government spending on 'Debt Interests' was 22.22% of the spending on 'Education services'.

The spending on 'Education services', 'Health services' and 'Debt Interests' constituted 50% of the **overall total** spending by the Government.

What was the Government's total spending? Write your answer to the nearest pound.

....

....

....

....

....

....

....

....

....

....

....

....

Answer = ...

(6 marks)

14. (a) Expand and simplify: $8(a + 6) + 11(a - 3)$

....

....

....

Answer = ...

(2 marks)

(b) Expand and simplify: $-10(8a - 4b)$

....

....

....

Answer = ...

(2 marks)

(c) Factorise fully: $x^2 - 16x + 64$

....

....

....

Answer = ...

(2 marks)

(d) Multiply out: $(y + 16)(y + 9)$

....

....

....

Answer = ...

(2 marks)

15. Below is a triangle.

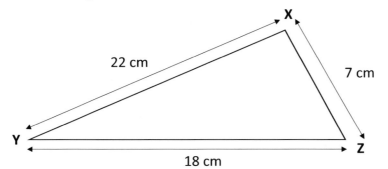

(a) Work out the area of the triangle. Write your answer to the nearest whole number.

....

....

Answer = ...

(2 marks)

(b) Make an accurate drawing where the base of the triangle is 6cm, with two angles of 48° and 64°.

(3 marks)

16. William is designing a wall mosaic which is to be placed in a local aquarium.

His mosaic contains 8 individual images, which are outlined by the grey rectangles on the below diagram.

The length of the mosaic is 8 metres. The height of the mosaic is 2 metres. The distance from the outer edge of the mosaic to the images is 20 cm. The distance around each image is also 20 cm.

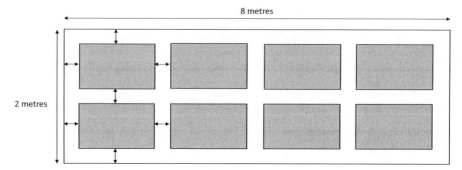

Each image is the exact same size. Using the information above, work out the length and height of the images.

....

....

....

....

....

....

....

....

....

Length ....

Height ....

(3 marks)

17. Below is a distance chart between five destinations.

The chart gives the driving distances, in kilometres.

				Destination A
			Destination B	245
		Destination C	796	425
	Destination D	375	168	157
Destination E	245	257	310	408

Harriett will be driving at an average speed of 65 mph.

How long, in hours and minutes, will it take Harriett to drive from Destination A to Destination B? Round your answer to the exact whole minute.

You must show **ALL** of your working out.

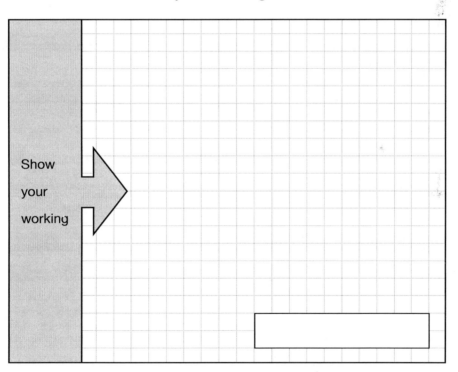

Show

your

working

(4 marks)

18. A swimming pool is a rectangular shape that is $2x$ in length.

The width of the swimming pool is $x - 4$.

The area of the swimming pool is 192 metres².

(a) Work out the value of x.

....

....

....

....

....

....

....

....

....

....

Answer = ...

(6 marks)

(b) Using your answer to part (a), and assuming the depth of the swimming pool is 1.5 metres, work out the volume of the swimming pool.

....

....

....

....

....

Answer = ...

(2 marks)

19. (a) Calculate the volume of a square-based pyramid of a height of 9.52 cm and a base length of 7.25 cm.

Give your answer to 3 decimal places.

....

....

....

....

Answer = ...

(4 marks)

(b) Below is a cylinder.

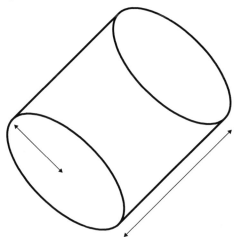

The radius of the cylinder is 9 cm.

The length of the cylinder is 16 cm.

Work out the surface area of the cylinder. Round all numbers up to 2 decimal places.

....

....

....

....

Answer = ...

(3 marks)

20. Abbie asked 500 children which zoo animal they preferred: lion, monkey, giraffe or elephant.

Of the 68 people who said their favourite animal was giraffe, 1/4 of them were male.

¾ of the total number of people surveyed said their favourite animal was monkey. 60% of which were female.

12 men and 15 women chose elephant as their favourite animal.

The rest of them said lion. The men to women ratio who chose lions was 4 : 1.

Work out how many men and how many women chose lion as their favourite animal.

You will be awarded marks for workings out.

....

....

....

....

....

....

....

(3 marks)

Men = ...

Women = ...

(2 marks)

21. You travel at an average speed of 62mph for 124 miles. You arrive at your destination, and spend 4 hours there before heading home. For your return journey, you travel at 40mph.

(a) How long were you away from home in total?

....

....

....

Answer = ...

(1 mark)

(b) How long was your return journey?

....

....

....

Answer = ...

(2 marks)

(c) How long was the first part of your journey?

....

....

....

Answer = ...

(2 marks)

GCSE

Mathematics

SET B

Calculator and Non-Calculator Paper
Higher Tier

ANSWER BOOKLET

Q1 (a) 4 Shape X is 4 times smaller than shape Y.	1 mark
Q1 (b) Your answer should look like this: 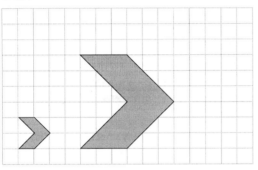	2 marks (1 mark for correct sizing of the shape). (1 mark for shading in the shape).
Q2 (a) 130 $13 \times 30 = 390$ $390 \div 3 = 130$	2 marks (1 mark for estimation that is no more than ± 2). (1 mark for showing all working outs with no errors).
Q2 (b) (i) 7 $^{11}/_{12}$ $4\,^2/_3 = \,^{14}/_3$ $3\,^1/_4 = \,^{13}/_4$ $(13 \times 3) + (4 \times 14)$ $39 + 56 = 95$ $(4 \times 3) = 12$ $^{95}/_{12} = 7\,^{11}/_{12}$	2 marks (1 mark for correct answer. Award no mark if the answer is not written as a mixed fraction). (1 mark for showing all workings out with no more than one error).

Q2 (b) (ii) $2\frac{5}{44}$ $31\frac{1}{4} \div 11\frac{1}{3}$ $(31 \times 3) \div (11 \times 4)$ $\frac{93}{44} = 2\frac{5}{44}$	2 marks (1 mark for correct answer. Award no mark if the answer is not written as a mixed fraction). (1 mark for showing all workings out with no more than one error).
Q3 (a) 7.6 $x^2 = 3^2 + 7^2$ $x^2 = 9 + 49$ $\sqrt{58} = 7.615$ To 1 dp = 7.6	2 marks (1 mark for correct answer). (1 mark for showing working out with no more than one error).
Q3 (b) 8 $x^2 = 10^2 - 6^2$ $x^2 = 100 - 36$ $\sqrt{64} = 8$	2 marks (1 mark for correct answer). (1 mark for showing working out with no more than one error).
Q4. £3,420 Self-catering holiday to Turkey for 5 people = 180 x 5 = 900. All-inclusive holiday to Mexico for 2 people = 720 x 2 = 1440. Booked three times = 1440 x 3 = 4320. So, 4320 – 900 = 3,420.	3 marks
Q5 (a) $y^2 - 10y$ Remove the brackets $y(y - 10)$ $y^2 - 10y$	1 mark
Q5 (b) $17x^2 - 4a - x$ $20x^2 - 8a - 3x^2 + 4a - x$ $17x^2 - 4a - x$	2 marks
Q5 (c) $6(3x^2 - 2)$ $18x^2 - 12$ $6(3x^2 - 2)$	2 marks

Q5 (d) $x = \dfrac{2y+2z}{a}$

You need to divide both sides by *a*.

2 marks

Q6 (a) 17 metres

Bathroom = 6m + (2 x 4 = 8) − (1 x 0.5 = 0.5) = 7.5

6 + 7.5 = 13.5

Kitchen = 1.5 + 2 = 3.5

13.5 + 3.5 = 17 metres

2 marks

Q6 (b) 680

Bathroom wall 1 = 240

Bathroom wall 2 = 300

Kitchen wall 1 = 60

Kitchen wall 2 = 80

3 marks

Q7 (a) 144 cm³

Volume of a triangular prism = area of triangle x length

4 x 6 x 12 = 288

288 ÷ 2 = 144 cm³

3 marks

Q7 (b) 40

If the width remains the same, but you want to work out how many prisms you will need to build a cuboid of a height of 80 cm:

1 prism = 4 cm in height.

1 cuboid = 2 prisms.

80 ÷ 4 = 20 (but remember you need 2 prisms to make up 1 cuboid, so this needs to be doubled = 20 x 2 = 40).

3 marks

Q8. x = 34

Angles in a parallelogram add up to 360°.

Opposite angles are equal.

4 marks

Q9 (a) 12 x 10^{500} $(4 \times 3) \times (10^{100} \times 10^{400})$ $12 \times 10^{100+400}$	2 marks
Q9 (b) 8.56 x 10^5	2 marks
Q9 (c) 4.85 x 10^{-3}	2 marks
Q10 (a) Eighty nine thousand three hundred and seven *The best way to write out the number is to read it out loud.*	1 mark
10. (b) (i) 89,310 *To the nearest 10, the number 89,307 will be rounded up to 89,310.* *The '7' in the units column determines what happens to the number in the tens column.*	1 mark
10. (b) (ii) 89,300 *To the nearest 100, the number 89,307 will be rounded down to 89,300.* *The number '0' in the tens column determines what happens to the number in the hundreds column.*	1 mark
(b) (iii) 89,000 *To the nearest 1,000, the number 89,307 will be rounded down to 89,000.* *The number '3' in the hundreds column determines what happens to the number in the thousands column.*	1 mark
Q11 (a) 4 m/s $8 \div 2 = 4$	2 marks

Q11 (b) 16 seconds

1 second per 4 m/s.
So 64 ÷ 4 = 16 seconds

3 marks
(1 mark for correct answer).
(2 marks for showing working out with no more than one error).

Q12. 11 hours and 28 minutes

English = 15 x 16 = 240 (4 hours)
Science = 14 x 32 = 448 (7 hours and 28 minutes)
4 hours + 7 hours and 28 minutes = 11 hours and 28 minutes

4 marks
(1 mark for correct answer).
(1 mark for writing answer in hours and minutes).
(1 mark for working out English).
(1 mark for working out Science).

Q13 (a) 260 degrees

3 marks

Q13 (b) 35 kilometres

3 marks

Q14 (a) 1103.3

1 mark

Q14 (b) 324.5

1 mark

Q14 (c) 11.033

1 mark

Q14 (d) 32450

1 mark

Q14 (e) 110.33

1 mark

Q15 (a) + 20, x8

x + 20 x 8
(x + 20) x 8
8(x + 20)

2 marks
(1 mark for correct answer).
(1 mark for showing working out).

Q15 (b) 128

-4 + 20 = 16
16 x 8 = 128

2 marks

Q16. Store C offers the best value

Store A = 420 + 33.50 + 112 + 12.50
= £578

Store B = 550 + 20 + 84.90 = £654.90

Store C = 320 + 20 + 80 = 420

$\qquad$ 420 ÷ 100 x 120 = 504

$\qquad$ 504 + 13 = £517

Therefore Store C offers the best value.

3 marks

(1 mark for correct answer).

(2 marks for showing working out. Deduct 1 mark for each error).

Q17 (a) -2, 0, 2, 4, 6, 8

2 marks

(1 mark for every two correct answers filled in).

Q17 (b) (-3, -4) (-2, -2,) (-1, 0) (0, 2) (1, 4)

3 marks

(3 marks for all correct points. Deduct 1 mark for each incorrect point. There should be at least 4 point marked on the grid).

Q18. (a) Your answer should look like this:

3 marks

(2 marks for filling in the table with no more than one error).

(1 mark for completing the key).

1	1 2 3 9
2	9
3	0 1 5 7 8 8 9
4	0
5	0 5 7
6	3 5 7 8 8 9
7	3 8 9
8	0 4 5
9	0 4

KEY:

1 | 1 = 11

Q18 (b) 56

The two numbers in the middle are 55 and 57

So 55 + 57 = 112

112 ÷ 2 = 56

1 mark

Q18 (c) 53

Add up all of the totals = 1597
1597 ÷ 30 = 53.23
To the nearest whole number = 53

1 mark

Q18 (d) 83

Biggest number (94) − smallest number (11) = 83

1 mark

Q18 (e) 47%

14 ÷ 30 x 100 = 46.666
To the nearest whole number = 47%

1 mark

Q19 (a) The mark for the airport should be drawn at an angle of 45° (using North as 0 degrees). The mark should be drawn 8 cm from the point of Sandy Beach.

1 mark

Q19 (b) The mark for the zoo should be drawn at an angle of 215° (using North as a 0 degrees). The mark should be drawn 4 cm from the point of Joy Town.

2 marks

Q20 (a) Your answer should look like this:

2 marks

```
10    15    20    25    30    35    40    45    50    55
```

Q20 (b) The boys struggled with the brain teaser more so than the girls. The boy's longest time was 56 seconds, whereas the girls' longest time was 52.

2 marks
(Any logical comparison between the two diagrams can score 2 marks. Comparisons in relation to longest time, shortest time or median time will score 2 marks).

Q21 (a) represent two consecutive numbers as n + *(n + 1)*.

So, an example: 3 + (3 + 1)

3 + 4 = 7 = this demonstrates that the total is odd.

Another example: 6 + (6 + 1)

6 + 7 = 13

Therefore Jordan's statement is true.

3 marks

(1 mark for showing how Jordan's statement is true).

(1 mark for using an example).

(1 mark for using algebra).

Q21 (b) Gemma is correct

Represent three consecutive numbers as n + (n + 1) + (n + 2)

An example = 4 + (4+1) + (4+2)

4 + 5 + 6 (consecutive numbers) = 15

15 is divisible by 3.

Another example = 12 + (12 + 1) + (12 + 2)

12 + 13 + 14 = 39

39 is divisible by 3.

Therefore Gemma is correct.

3 marks

(2 marks for working out that Gemma is correct).

(1 mark for using an example).

Q1 (a) 6, 15, 24, 33, 42, 51	2 marks
Replace the n with which terms in the sequence you are working out.	(2 marks for all correct answers. Award 1 mark if there is one mistake.
For example, to find the 1st term:	No marks to be awarded if there is more than one mistake).
9×1 (1st term) $= 9 - 3 = 6$	
Q1 (b) (i) 3	2 marks
3rd term $= 27$	(1 mark for correct answer).
2nd term $= 27 - 5 = 22$	(1 mark for showing working out).
$\qquad 22 \div 2 = 11$	
1st term $= 11 - 5 = 6$	
$\qquad 6 \div 2 = 3$	
Q1 (b) (ii) 59, 123, 251, 507	1 mark
Remember, double previous term and then add 5.	
Q2 First graph = x = 4	3 marks
Second graph = x = y	(1 mark for each correct equation).
Third graph = y = x + 3	
Q3. The total frequency is 90. That means you can multiply each frequency by 4 in order to get a whole circle of 360°.	4 marks
	(1 mark for each correct segment drawn on the pie chart).
Football = 31 x 4 = 124	
Tennis = 24 x 4 = 96	
Rounders = 16 x 4 = 64	
Dance = 15 x 4 = 60	
Hockey = 4 x 4 = 16	
Your answer should be measured accurately using a protractor.	

Q4. 230.88

Area of a circle = Pi x radius^2

Radius of the circle = 7 ÷ 2 = 3.5

3.5^2 = 12.25

Pi x 12.25 = 38.4845

To 2 decimal places = 38.48

38.48 x 6 = 230.88

5 marks

(1 mark for correct answer).

(1 mark for working out radius).

(1 mark for working out radius squared).

(1 mark for working out the decimal to two decimal places).

(1 mark for multiplying the decimal by the number of circles).

Q5. (a) 0.65

¼ = 25% + 10% = 35%

100 − 35 = 65% = 0.65

1 mark

Q5 (b) English = 1 hour and 18 minutes

Maths = 12 minutes

Test 1 = 15 minutes

Test 2 = 15 minutes

2 hours = 120 minutes

Spends ¼ of time divided equally between the two mini tests (120 ÷ 4 = 30) (30 ÷ 2 = 15 minutes per mini test)

English = 65% = 120 ÷ 100 x 65 = 78 minutes (1 hour and 18 minutes)

Maths = 10% = 120 ÷ 100 x 10 = 12 minutes

78 + 15 + 15 + 12 = 120 minutes (2 hours)

2 marks

(1 mark for every two correct answers).

Q6. x = 20°

4 marks

(1 mark for correct answer)

(3 marks for showing working out. Deduct one mark for each error that occurs).

Q7. x = 2.8

Replace x with a number and keep trying until you find the number that completes the solution.

$2.8^3 - 4 \times 2.8 =$

$21.952 - 11.2 = 10.75$

4 marks

(1 mark for correct answer)

(1 mark for correct answer to 1 decimal place).

(2 marks for trial and improvement).

Q8 (a) £485,100

$412,500 \div 100 \times 112 = 462,000$

$462,000 \div 100 \times 105 = 485,100$

2 marks

(1 mark for correct answer).

(1 mark for showing working out).

Q8 (b) £84,159.35

$765,085 \div 100 \times 89 = £680,925.65$

So the difference = $765,085 -$
$680,925.65 = £84,159.35$

2 marks

(1 mark for correct answer).

(1 mark for showing working out).

Q9. 6 years

$7000 \div 100 \times 106.8 = 7476 = 1$ year

$7476 \div 100 \times 106.8 = 7984 = 2$ years

$7984 \div 100 \times 106.8 = 8526 = 3$ years

$8526 \div 100 \times 106.8 = 9105 = 4$ years

$9105 \div 100 \times 106.8 = 9724 = 5$ years

$9724 \div 100 \times 106.8 = 10385 = 6$ years

3 marks

(1 mark for correct answer).

(2 marks for showing working out with no more than one error).

Q10. 150,000,000 km

1.5×10^{11} ($10 \times 10 \times 10 \times 10 \times 10$
$\times 10 \times 10 \times 10 \times 10 \times 10 \times 10$) =
150000000000 m

150000000000 m $\div$ 1,000 =
150000000 km.

4 marks

(1 mark for correct answer).

(2 marks for working out with no more than one error).

(1 mark for writing converting answer to kilometres).

Q11 (a) $\sqrt{1600} \times 50 - 72$ has the greater value

$20 \times (5) + (64 \times 25)$

$100 + 1600 = 1700$

$\sqrt{1600} = 40 \times 50 = 2000$

$2000 - 72 = 1928$

Therefore the second calculation has the greater value.

3 marks

(1 mark for correct answer).

(1 mark for showing workings out).

(1 mark for quality of written communication).

Q11 (b) If 25% compound interest is added per year, and Lena is able to pay off the loan in 4 years, she will be paying over double what she borrowed.

1600 ÷ 100 x 125 = 2000 (1 year)

2000 ÷ 100 x 125 = 2500 (2 year)

2500 ÷ 100 x 125 = 3125 (3 years)

3125 ÷ 100 x 125 = 3906.25 (4 years)

3906.25 is over double 1600 (which is what Lena borrowed originally).

3 marks

(1 mark for correct answer).

(1 mark for showing workings out).

(1 mark for quality of written communication).

Q12 (a) 2

Each flat part of the graph shows zero acceleration.

1 mark

Q12 (b) 7.5

Area under graph = distance travelled = ½ x base x height = ½ x 1 x 15 = 7.5 km.

1 mark

Q12 (c) 6 hours

15 km/h = 1 hour

100 ÷ 15 = 6

2 marks

(1 mark for correct answer).

(1 mark for showing working out).

Q13. 351 billion pounds

Education services = 56.3 billion pounds and

Health services = 106.7 billion pounds.

22.22% of 56.3 = 56.3 ÷ 100 x 22.22 = 12.50986 (Round up = 12.51).

The total of Education, Health and Debt Interests = 175.51 billion pounds.

The total Government spending = 175.51 x 100 ÷ 50 = 351.02.

So, the approximate total = 351 billion pounds.

6 marks

(1 mark for correct answer).

(5 marks for showing working out. Deduct one mark for each error that occurs).

Q14 (a) 19a + 15 $8a + 48 + 11a - 33$ $19a + 15$	2 marks (1 mark for correct answer). (1 mark for showing working out).
Q14 (b) -80a + 40b	2 marks (1 mark for correct answer). (1 mark for showing working out).
Q14 (c) (x – 8) (x + 8)	2 marks (1 mark for correct answer). (1 mark for showing working out).
Q14 (d) $y^2 + 25y + 144$ $(y + 16) (y + 9)$ $y^2 + 9y + 16y + 144$ $y^2 + 25y + 144$	2 marks (1 mark for correct answer). (1 mark for showing working out).
Q15 (a) 57 cm² $22 + 7 + 18 = 47$ $47 \div 2 = 23.5$ $23.5 \times 1.5 \times 16.5 \times 5.5 = 3198.93$ To the nearest whole number = 3199 $\sqrt{3199} = 56.55$ To the nearest whole number = 57 cm²	2 marks (1 mark for correct answer). (1 marks for working out with no more than one error).
Q15 (b) The triangle must have a base drawn of 6cm. Two angles should measure at 48° and 64°. The other angle would therefore measure to be 68°.	3 marks (1 mark for drawing the base exactly 6cm). (1 mark per correct angle).

Q16. Length = 1 metre 75 centimetres

   Height = 70 centimetres

800 – 20 – 20 – 20 – 20 – 20 = 700

700 ÷ 4 = 175 centimetres (1.75 metres)

200 – 20 – 20 – 20 = 140

140 ÷ 2 = 70 centimetres

3 marks

(1 mark for working out length).

(1 mark for working out height).

(1 mark for showing working out with no more than one error).

Q17. 2 hours and 20 minutes

4 marks

(Award 1 mark for correct answer).

(Award 1 mark for correctly converting kilometres into miles).

(Award 2 marks for correctly dividing the distance by speed).

Q18 (a) x = 12

6 marks

(2 marks for correct answer).

(4 marks for showing all working out. Deduct one mark for each error in calculation).

Q18 (b) 144

24 x 4 x 1.5

2 marks

(1 mark for correct answer).

(1 mark for showing working out).

Q19 (a) 166.798

Volume of a pyramid = 1/3 x (base area) x height

1/3 x (7.25 x 7.25) x 9.52

52.5625 x 9.52 = 500.395

500.395 ÷ 3 = 166.79833…

To 3 decimal places = 166.798

4 marks

(1 mark for correct answer).

(3 marks for showing working out. Deduct one mark each error in calculation).

Q19 (b) 16285.76 cm

2 x Pi x 9^2

81 x 2 x Pi = 508.93

508.93 + 508.93 = 1017.86

1017.86 x 16 = 16285.76

3 marks

(1 mark for correct answer).

(2 marks for showing working out. Deduct one mark each error in calculation).

Q20. Men = 24, Women = 6

$500 \div 4 \times 3 = 375$

$500 - 375 = 125$

$125 - 68 = 57$

$57 - 12 - 15 = 30$

$30 \div 5 = 6$ ($6 \times 4 = 24$ (men)) ($6 \times 1 = 6$ (women))

5 marks

(3 marks for wo

(2 marks for cor

Q21 (a) 9 hours and 6 minutes

2 hours + 3 hours 6 minutes + 4 hours = 9 hours 6 minutes

1 mark

Q21 (b) 3 hours and 6 minutes

$124 \div 40 = 3.1$

The .1 represents 6 minutes (60 minutes $\div$ 10 = 6).

Therefore the return journey is 3 hours and 6 minutes.

2 marks

(1 mark for correct answer).

(1 mark for showing working out).

Q21 (c) 2 hours

62 miles per hour

2 hours = 124 miles

2 marks

(1 mark for correct answer).

(1 mark for showing working out).

IMPROVE YOUR MATHEMATICAL ABILITY!

FURTHER YOUR LEARNING!

How2Become have created these FANTASTIC guides to help you fully prepare for GCSE languages – French and Spanish with ease!

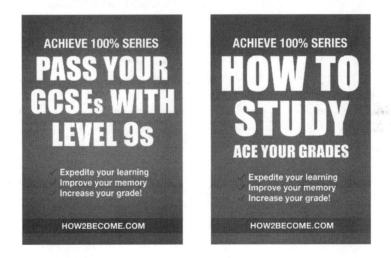

Take a look at our 'Achieve 100%' series. Improve your learning with the help of these proven study resources.

FOR MORE INFORMATION ON OUR GCSE GUIDES, PLEASE VISIT:

WWW.HOW2BECOME.COM

Get Access To
FREE
GCSE
TEST QUESTIONS

www.MyEducationalTests.co.uk